LIVING CONTROL SYSTEMS

LIVING
CONTROL SYSTEMS

L. E. BAYLISS
B.A., Ph.D.

Formerly Department of Physiology, University College,
London

W. H. FREEMAN AND COMPANY
SAN FRANCISCO

First printed 1966

W. H. FREEMAN AND COMPANY

Printed in Great Britain

PREFACE

The author of this book, Leonard Bayliss, died in August 1964. For many years, up to 1959, he had worked incessantly in producing, in two volumes, a new edition of his father's great work, *Principles of General Physiology*, published first in 1915. In his patience, his helpfulness, and his inexhaustible knowledge, he was singularly like W.M.B.; and the company of physiologists everywhere is greatly indebted to him for preserving his father's thought, and extending it in more modern guise for a further many years.

When Bayliss had finished this major task his mind went back to things in which he had been active during the war. From 1940 to 1945 he was an important member of the Army Operational Research Group, and had been concerned with the control of anti-aircraft guns and their accessory instruments. As he points out on p. 7 it was only in 1930 that a rigorous theoretical study had begun of how automatic control systems work and how they should be designed.

Naturally, as he saw these systems develop rapidly during the war, he reflected on their many counterparts in living systems, where they had evolved slowly, to supreme perfection, over hundreds of millions of years. So when he returned to physiology he began to put together his thoughts on the subject and between 1960 and 1964 devoted much of his time to writing them down. Fortunately the work had already been completed when he died.

It is no new idea that living organisms contain numerous self-regulating control systems, but we are only now beginning to understand the factors that govern the sensitivity, speed of response and stability of these elaborate mechanisms. An immense field still awaits exploration here, both by biologists who acquire a sufficient understanding of the theory of automatic mechanisms that has been developed by engineers, and by people trained as engineers or mathematicians who come to realise what a fascinating variety of "living control systems" are waiting to be investigated.

In a letter to Sir Graham Sutton, General Editor of this series, Bayliss wrote that, when writing this book, he "had in mind that its readers might be, primarily, at the level of the sixth form at schools and the first year at Universities whose training had been either on the mathematico-physical side, or on the biological side; and secondly some more advanced students in experimental biology and engineering". This statement is characteristic of Bayliss's modesty, and of his generosity in estimating the abilities of the young: in addition to its value at the levels that he mentions, this book will bring a new order of understanding of living things to a wide range of general readers with some training in physical or biological science, and indeed will also be an admirable introduction for established research workers who wish to enter this field from either the biological or the engineering side.

Bayliss also recognised the difficulty of writing for two groups of readers: "this implies that one half of the readers will find some parts of the book familiar and possibly unnecessary and the other half will find the other part to be equally familiar and unnecessary". But there cannot be many biologists who are familiar with all the examples from the animal and vegetable worlds that he brings forward, and on the other side, few but the servo experts will fail to benefit from the lucid account of control theory that is given here.

A. V. HILL
A. F. HUXLEY

CONTENTS

1 AUTOMATIC CONTROL

Animals and plants are chemical factories. They take in raw material from their surroundings, convert part into various kinds of finished product, and use the remainder to provide power for conversion. Animals, in addition, are provided with engines which enable them to move about: the factory can move, when necessary, to its source of raw material, or escape from rivals who seek to devour it.

Just as in an industrial concern, the conversion and fabrication processes are managed and controlled. A factory is so organised that it makes only those things which it sets out to make, and that these things are of the intended size, shape and composition: further, the intake of raw material and power is controlled so as to match the rate at which they are used in the factory. In industry this management and control is ordinarily done by skilled men and women in the office staff and at the machines in the shops; "automation", however, seeks to replace these men and women by "automatic control systems". Similarly, in the world of living things animals and plants grow and develop in such a way that each kind attains, and maintains, its proper size and shape. The various parts—organs and tissues—of which it is made up are constrained to work in such a way as to co-operate with one another for the well-being of the whole animal or plant. The working of these parts and the behaviour of the whole animal or plant are adjusted and controlled in response to changes in the external world in which it lives.

According to the "vitalists" such regulation and control, particularly of growth and development, are performed by some "vital force" quite different from anything in the non-living world; it would be futile to try to investigate this by the methods of experimental science. Few biologists would now be so dogmatic: there is at least no harm in trying to describe how living plants and animals work in the same sort of way that we describe how non-living machines and chemical factories work. From this point of view, regulation and control in the living world depend on the existence of automatic control systems. Engineers have made extensive studies of the general principles on which these must be designed if they are to work properly: we shall try to find out whether these same principles can be used to account for the performance of living control systems.

Some simple examples of automatic control

To begin with, let us describe a few devices which may properly be called automatic control systems. One of the earliest of these is the governor which James Watt (1736–1819) put on his steam engines. The amount of steam which is fed to the engine must be made to depend on the load to be overcome; if too little, the engine stalls, if too much, it races and perhaps damages itself. A throttle valve, accordingly, is placed in the steam supply pipe. The amount of steam flowing to the engine will depend, also, on the pressure in the boiler, and this will vary with the diligence of the stoker, as well as on the amount of steam needed by the engine to drive the load. The governor, therefore, has to take into account both the load and the steam pressure. It does this, not by attempting to measure both directly, but by detecting changes in the speed of the engine, opening the throttle when the speed falls and closing it when the speed rises; counteracting, in other words, any departure or "misalignment" from the desired speed or "set-point".

Another example, more familiar but much cruder, is the ball-valve in the domestic water tank. This detects changes in the level of water in the tank, admitting water from the mains whenever the level falls as a result of water being drawn off through the taps: the flow from the mains is thus kept equal to the total flow from all the taps, each of which may be opened or shut in an unpredictable way. But suppose that it was the inflow to the tank that was adjusted arbitrarily, and not the outflow from it: suppose, for example, that the bath-taps are turned on without inserting the plug in the waste-pipe. Within limits set by the height of the bath, the level of water will rise until the outflow down the waste-pipe is the same as the inflow from the taps. Again inflow and outflow become equal, but the system cannot properly be called a control system. The outflow is not regulated or adjusted so as to be equal to the inflow, but happens to become so owing to the inherent properties of the system: most automatic control systems work in conditions where there is no such tendency towards stabilisation—indeed their chief value is in conditions where the inherent tendency is in the other way, towards a "run-away" to some extreme state, as in an engine without any form of governor.

So far we have assumed that the fluctuations in demand that the control system has to cope with are random, without any particular pattern. But in some of the most valuable kinds of control system this is not so: they are given definite instructions which they have to act on precisely, and they do this in the same way as those already described, by comparing the results of their activities (their "output" as it is called) with the instructions given them (their "input") and ensuring that the difference between them (the misalignment or "error") is zero, or as close to zero as possible. (The terms "input" and "output" of a control system are sometimes confusing: the input to the ball-valve of the water tank is the water level, lowered by an outflow of water; the output is the movement of the valve which controls the inflow of water). Such a control system is called a "follow-up servo-system", and an example is to be found in an automatic machine tool, which is fabricating parts of a particular size and shape from, say, a bar of steel. Ordinarily, the operator of the machine controls the movement of the cutting tools by hand, checking the dimensions of the part being made from time to time against those on a drawing provided. In an automatic machine, the instructions on the drawing are fed to servo-systems which control motors, advancing or withdrawing the cutting tools until the shape and size of the part correspond to those on the instructions— i.e. until the misalignment is zero. A similar kind of system can easily be imagined as controlling the whole operations of the factory, replacing the inspectorate, for example, which examines the product, rejects that which is incorrect, and issues instructions which remove the source of the rejects.

Automatic control in living beings

The study of living control systems may be said to begin with the work and thought of the great French physiologist Claude Bernard (1813–1878). In the summer of 1870 he gave a course of lectures in the Natural History Museum of Paris; these were published in 1878, just after his death, under the title "Lessons on the Phenomena of Life common to Animals and Vegetables".

The second Lesson (the third after an "Introductory Lesson") is headed: "The Three Forms of Life": first, "Latent life" as in seeds, eggs and some kinds of animalcule which have temporarily "fallen into a state of chemical indifference" on being dried for instance; secondly "oscillating (or fluctuating) life", as in rather primitive animals and plants whose activity and behaviour depend greatly on the nature of their surroundings; and thirdly, the "free and independent life", best seen in the most highly developed animals which are little affected by changes in the physical and chemical properties of their surroundings. In this Lesson, also, Claude Bernard introduces the idea that the living cells which make up an animal (and also a plant) are not in contact with the "external" environment—the air, sea or lake in which it lives—but with an "internal" environment consisting of a watery solution often quite different in composition from that of the outside solution. "The constancy of the internal environment is the condition that life should be free and independent." This constancy, however, does not mean that the animal is shut off from its surroundings and unaffected by them. "So far from the higher animal being indifferent to the external world, it is on the contrary in a precise and informed (*étroite et savante* are the words actually used) relation with it, in such a way that its equilibrium results from a continuous and delicate compensation, established as by the most sensitive of balances." This passage might be paraphrased in more modern terminology as: "The higher animals possess control systems which adjust the interactions and exchanges with their surroundings in such a way that the physical state and chemical composition of the internal environment remains constant."

Claude Bernard's ideas were taken up and developed by the English physiologist Joseph Barcroft (1872–1947) in a series of lectures delivered at Harvard University, U.S.A., in 1929 and published in 1934 under the title "Features in the Architecture of Physiological Function". In 1929, also, the American physiologist W. B. Cannon (1871–1945) introduced the word "homeostasis" (from the Greek, meaning literally "similar-standing") to describe, generally, all the processes concerned in controlling the physical and chemical properties of the internal environment of an animal. He developed and extended his ideas in a book "The Wisdom of the Body", published in 1932. The titles of these books emphasise the fact that control of the internal environment is essential to the whole design and organisation of an animal, ensuring that its component parts work in co-operation with one another.

The extent to which life is entirely "free and independent" will depend on the precision of the control systems concerned. There are likely to be many of these, so that homeostasis may be more perfect in some respects than in others. There is no hard and fast dividing line between Claude Bernard's second and third forms of life: there are animals whose life is "free and independent" in respect, say, of the salt concentration of their body fluids, but "fluctuating" in respect of their temperatures. In studying homeostasis in any of its various aspects, our task is to discover which of the various activities, both internal and external, of the animal or plant are controlled—i.e. the nature of the input and output of each of the control systems concerned; how the mis-alignment between them is detected and corrected; and how accurately the system works. This is done chiefly by applying the methods of experimental physiology, together with some of those of biophysics and biochemistry. But a proper interpretation of the results requires, also, some knowledge of the fundamental theory of control systems.

Study of the growth and development of animals and plants into the "proper" size, shape and general behaviour is based on the methods of experimental embryology and biochemical genetics more than on those of experimental physiology. These have existed only for some 30 to 50 years, while the idea that automatic control systems of the "follow-up" type are in action is much more recent still. Here we must discover how the "information"—as on a drawing or blue-print—is conveyed to the control systems, as well as the mode of action of the systems themselves.

Servo systems

The type of automatic control system with which we are concerned may be represented schematically in the "block diagram" of *Figure 1*. If the "input element" is moved, say to the right, the "controller" is activated, power is directed to the "motor" and the "output element" is moved, also to the right. This movement is sent back to the controller by means of the "feedback element" and is subtracted from the movement of the input element (the feedback is "negative"). When the output element has moved through the same distance as the input element, the difference between them—"misalignment" or "error"—is zero, the controller is no longer activated and the motor comes to rest. It is

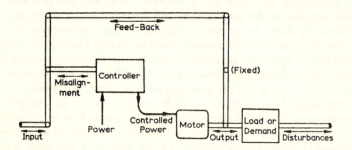

FIGURE I   *Block diagram of simple control system.*

(L. E. Bayliss, 1960. "Principles of General Physiology," Longmans, Green and Co.)

the presence of the feedback element, the introduction of a "closed loop", and the activation of the motor by the misalignment between input and output that are characteristic of a "servo system". The input and output elements do not necessarily move to and fro only; they may rotate continuously, for example, the controller and motor then keeping them in step. Or the rotating shafts may be replaced by a flow of heat, water or any other substance: the "motor" may, for example, be the cooling unit of a domestic refrigerator, pumping heat out of the food, or a pump lifting water from a well to a tank at the top of the house. By introducing a second subtracting mechanism we can arrange that the motor ceases to be activated only when the misalignment—the temperature within the refrigerator or the amount of water in the reservoir—is equal to some pre-determined "set-point", not necessarily zero. Such a servo system is obviously of the kind that may be expected to be concerned in homeostasis and the preservation of the constancy of the internal environment of an animal. The set-point, also, may be varied, arbitrarily or according to some "programme", and we have a follow-up system such as that needed to control growth and development.

Designing and analysing servo systems

When an engineer is designing a system which is to control

some particular process or machine, he puts together a number of different components, whose properties he knows, aiming to build up a complete system with a performance which is good enough for the purpose. The biologist's problem is somewhat different. He is presented with an intact and functioning control system; he probably has some idea as to the properties of some, at least, of the components and he wants to find out whether these components, if put together, make up a system which is at least approximately similar to the complete system that he is interested in. If it is not, he must look for further components with suitable properties, and try again. His procedure, therefore, and method of study are similar to those of the engineer. Both must put together a number of components, whose properties may have to be measured experimentally; and they must discover, mathematically, graphically, or possibly by some form of experiment, the overall properties of the resulting system.

Although engineers have been using automatic control systems for a great many years, rigorous theoretical study of how they work and of how to design them so that they work as well as possible, only began in about 1930.

Transfer functions. Each component of the complete system receives an "input signal"—is "excited" by some "stimulus"— and emits an "output signal" or "response" which is determined by the stimulus but is not necessarily, or usually, identical with it. The response of one component, at any moment, may be proportional to the magnitude of the stimulus at that moment; that of another may depend on the rate of change of the stimulus; some other component may not respond immediately the stimulus is given, but only after a period of delay. Lastly, the motor may drive a load with inertia and viscous friction which determine the relation between the motion of the output element, the force exerted by the motor, and the excitation given to it. The relation between the response of any of these components and the excitatory stimulus given to it—i.e. the kind of change that occurs in the signal as it is transferred from one end of the component to the other—is described by its *transfer function*, commonly and most concisely written in the form of mathematical "short-hand", the size of the response, the size of the stimulus, the rate of change of the stimulus, and so on, being represented by appropriate mathematical symbols. But transfer functions may also be represented graphically by means of lines drawn on squared paper: the size

of the response may be plotted against the size of the stimulus, or
against the rate of change of the stimulus; the ratio of the response
to the stimulus at any moment may be plotted against time after
the stimulus is given; and other rather less obvious methods of
plotting the graphs may be used as being more suitable and convenient, as will appear later.

When various components are connected together to form a
complete servo system, the input, or stimulus, to each is the
output, or response, of the one before it. If in *Figure 1* we detach
the feed-back element ("open the loop"), the relation between the
output of the system and the input to it—which in these circumstances is also the misalignment—will be defined by the
product of the transfer functions of all the components in the
system, multiplied together. This is known as the "*loop* transfer
function". When the feed-back element is put back again, the
relation between output and misalignment will still be defined
by the loop transfer function, but the relation between output
and input, defined by the "*overall transfer function*", will be
different, since input is misalignment *plus* output.

Linear and non-linear transfer functions. Suppose that we plot the
size of the response given by some component against the size of
the stimulus applied to it. If the plotted points all lie on a straight
line which passes through the origin, the response being zero
only when the stimulus is zero, the transfer function of the
component is said to be "linear". This would be so, also, if we
found, for example, that the response was proportional to the
rate of change (velocity) of the stimulus, instead of proportional
to the size of the stimulus, or to the rate of change of the rate of
change (acceleration) of the stimulus. But if the plotted points
did not lie on a straight line through the origin, so that the
response/stimulus ratio depended on the magnitude of the
stimulus, the transfer function would be "non-linear". This is
the most common form of non-linearity in the components of
both living and non-living systems. A different form of non-
linearity occurs when the transfer function changes with time,
and the positions of the plotted points depend on the time which
has passed since the stimulus was applied. Both these kinds of
non-linearity will be discussed more fully in later chapters.

Non-linear systems possess many useful properties which are
absent in linear systems. All practical systems, moreover, both
living and non-living, are non-linear when driven to their limits,

even though in their ordinary operating conditions they may behave as if they were very nearly linear. The theory of linear control systems is much easier than that of non-linear ones; we start by assuming linearity and then, if necessary, study the consequences of adding various kinds of non-linearity.

Testing servo systems

If we are provided with an intact and functioning servo system, we discover its properties, to begin with, by observing and measuring the changes in its output which accompany known changes in its input. (We may find, later, that we have to take it to pieces and measure, also, the properties of its components). We then try to design a servo system, using components with known transfer functions, which behaves in a similar way. We know the overall transfer function of any system that we have designed, so that if we know how the input varies with time, we can, in principle, calculate how the output varies with time. But unless the system is an extremely simple one, the necessary mathematical procedures are likely to be difficult, laborious, or even impossible by rigid and exact methods. (In mathematical terms, the overall transfer function is a differential equation, and this has to be solved, after inserting an expression defining the nature of the input used.) The same problem arises, of course, when an engineer has to design a system which satisfies some particular criteria as to its performance.

We can avoid part of the difficulty by using for our test measurements one or other of two simple kinds of input signal: a sudden ("step function") displacement, or change in velocity (the latter being known also as a "ramp function", since the displacement-time curve is a sloping straight line); or oscillatory (simple harmonic) motions with a suitable range of different frequencies.

The frequency (or harmonic) response method has certain advantages over the use of step or ramp functions, at least for studying non-living systems; it is often difficult or impossible to apply oscillatory inputs to living systems, although this has been done and some examples will be given in Chapter 7. When the input is a simple harmonic motion, the transfer functions of the components may easily be drawn on graph paper: a "model" servo system may then be built up, also on paper, by applying certain simple rules by which the transfer functions are multiplied together graphically. The resulting curves give relations between output and input which can be compared with the results of measurements on an actual working system. No mathematics are needed for this; but some simple mathematics are needed in order to draw the graphs for components of known properties and to discover the rules of procedure.

The response of a complete system to a step function input, on the other hand, when plotted graphically, shows how the output changes when the input is changed from one steady position, or velocity, to another; it gives, probably, a rather more obvious picture of the properties of the system as it is likely to behave in practice. But in order to draw these graphs, the transfer functions of the components must be multiplied together algebraically and the resulting overall transfer function solved mathematically: even with such a simple kind of input signal it may be advisable, or even necessary, to use approximate graphical or numerical methods of solution and to make use of computers.

Numerical methods consist in principle of replacing the exact mathematical operations necessary for a complete solution of the equation by a succession of simple arithmetical procedures—in the last analysis, by a succession of additions (or subtractions). The number of these increases with the complexity of the equation to be solved and with the accuracy required in the solution: in the past, the time and labour involved have been formidable. Much of this trouble is avoided by the use of *digital computers* which work so rapidly that it is quite feasible to use them for performing calculations which involve millions of simple additions. Working out the "instructions" or "programme" for the computer, however, needs specialist knowledge and may take quite a long time.

The *analogue computer*, on the other hand, known also in this connection as a "servo simulator", is in effect a working model of a complete control system. It is convenient, when constructing a simulator, to use electrical and electromechanical components which have the same properties (in respect of their transfer functions) as those in the actual control system to be constructed, or with which the model is to be compared. The biologist often cannot use the actual living components conveniently; nor, possibly, can the engineer use his actual components when he is designing, say, a large hydraulic system, or a system which is to control a chemical reaction process. Electrical (including electronic) components can easily be inserted, taken away, or exchanged for others; electrical signals can be added, subtracted, multiplied, divided and subjected to the mathematical operations of integration and differentiation, without difficulty; and the components can be constructed so as to have non-linear properties of almost any desired kind. The design of simulators is quite a specialised kind of study, involving considerable knowledge of electronics, which we cannot go into here.

A simulator, constructed to some particular design, may be given any kind of input signal, and its output observed. Records, for example, may be taken over a suitable period of time of the misalignment and output (or rate of change of output) of a living control system in action in its normal surroundings. The recorded misalignments may then be "played back" through the simulator, whose components are adjusted until it gives, as far as reasonably possible, the same output as did the living system. It is usually preferable, nevertheless, to use step function or oscillating inputs, since it is then easier to infer from the output what kinds of change are needed in the components of the simulator.

2 THE COMPONENTS OF LIVING CONTROL SYSTEMS

The important, and essential, parts of a control system such as that represented in *Figure 1* are: (1) means whereby information about the position and movement of the input and output elements and the amount of misalignment is conveyed from one part of the system to another; (2) some devices for detecting and measuring the misalignment or departure from the set-point and possibly, also, for measuring the input and output; (3) the controller which adjusts the amount of power exerted by the motor and, to make the adjustment appropriate, performs various mathematical operations on the misalignment supplied to it; and (4) the motor which provides the power needed to move the load on the output element. All these have their counterparts in living systems.

Transmission of information

When engineers design control systems they do not, usually, convey information about the amounts and rates of input, output and misalignment from one part of the system to another by means of the movements of rods, as is implied in *Figure 1*: whatever the actual nature of the input and output—mechanical movements, flow of water or any other fluid, heat or electricity—the signals within the control system usually consist of variations in the pressure and flow of oil or air, or variations in electrical voltages and currents. Similarly, in living systems, the signals are conveyed either by means of "chemical messengers" or "hormones", diffusing from one cell to another, or carried by fluids (the circulating blood, if present) moving from one part of the animal or plant to another; or by means of "impulses", accompanied by electrical effects, transmitted relatively rapidly from cell to cell.

This second method of conveying information is rather uncommon in plants, and is known to occur only in those whose movements are sufficiently rapid to be easily observed—notably the "sensitive plant" *Mimosa pudica,* and various plants which trap insects such as the "Venus' fly-trap" *Dionaea muscipula.* In animals, for all practical purposes, it is restricted to the specialised structures of the nervous system, and the "impulses" are ordinarily known as "nerve impulses". Plants do not have nervous systems— at least not obviously—but there is every reason to suppose that the "impulses" are transmitted in essentially the same way.

Hormones are synthesised in animals by special secreting glands in response to nerve impulses in their "secretory nerves", or in response to the presence of some other hormone in the fluid surrounding them or in the blood flowing to them. In plants, also, they are synthesised by certain kinds of cell only, usually those in

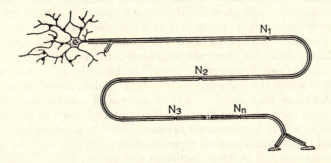

FIGURE 2 *A nerve fibre and the nerve cell from which it is derived.*

The fibre (axon) is shown with a myelin sheath (not actually quite so thick as is shown) which is interrupted at intervals by nodes of Ranvier, N_1, N_2, N_3, N_n. This sheath is present only in the rapidly conducting nerve fibres of vertebrates. The fibre is broken at one point, since, on the scale of the drawing, it may be 100 metres long. It is shown terminating on two "end-plates" which would be in contact with muscle fibres. The nature and fine structure of the ending depends on the kind of effector (or other nerve cell) which it excites.

The cell body is at the top, left, with fine processes (dendrites) extending out from it. A few synaptic "knobs" are shown in contact with the dendrites. The cell is excited through these by branches from other nerve fibres: these are actually many more than is shown. Alternatively, the dendrites may be in contact with receptor cells.

There are many nerve cells whose axons do not leave the nervous system, and are short, with many branches, very similar to the dendrites.

In the vertebrates, the receptor nerves are peculiar: the axon is continuous with one very long dendrite, similar in appearance to it, which is in contact with the receptor cells; the cell body is on a side branch close to the nervous system.

the growing tips of shoots and roots; but these do not have the same specialised structures as those of the secreting glands in animals.

The Nervous System. Although not strictly relevant to our theme, it will help later discussion of matters that are relevant if a brief description is given of what is known about the nature of the nerve impulse, how it is initiated, and why it is that so much has been discovered by electrical recording methods. In all kinds of animal the nervous system consists of a large number of nerve cells or "neurons" out of each of which extends a nerve fibre, or "axon"; the nerve cell is less than $\frac{1}{10}$ mm. in diameter, but the nerve fibre may be very long—up to several metres in large animals. Nerve impulses ordinarily travel along the axon away from the nerve cell towards the "nerve endings" in contact with another nerve cell, a muscle fibre or a secreting gland. The nerve fibre is something like an electric telegraph wire carrying signals in Morse code, but there are important differences. The signals are only of one kind—only "shorts" and no "longs"—and the code in which the "message" is conveyed consists, not of patterns of short and long impulses, but of patterns of varying intervals between successive impulses. A single message may be shared between a very large number of nerve fibres: its meaning is conveyed by the fraction of all these which are carrying impulses at any moment and by their particular connections at the "switchboards" in the nervous system as well as by the frequency of impulses in any one fibre.

Like all living cells, nerve cells and nerve fibres contain watery solutions of many different substances, and are surrounded by watery solutions. We are concerned at the moment only with the components of these solutions which are "electrolytes", consisting of atoms, or groups of atoms, which have positive or negative electric charges and are called "ions". Movement of the ions from one place to another, and thus also of their electric charges, gives rise to electric currents; an excess of ions of one sign in some region, and thus an excess of electric charge of that sign, gives rise to an electrical potential difference between that region and the surroundings. The electric charge carried by each ion is very large, and in the conditions in which nerve fibres are investigated, a detectable potential difference is produced by an excess of ions of one sign over those of the other of only one part in a thousand-million or so. Many different kinds of ion are present in these solutions, but we are chiefly interested in the cations (positively charged) of sodium and potassium.

All living cells so far investigated, and in particular nerve and other "excitable" cells, have the property of expelling sodium ions by means of a "sodium pump". We have, at present, little or no idea as to how this works, but it must be driven by some kind of an "engine" which gets most of its power, at least in the last analysis, from the combination with oxygen ("combustion") of the sugar glucose. If the anions (negatively charged) within the cell travelled along with the sodium ions (as one might expect, owing to the strong electrostatic attraction between them), there would soon be very little of the contents of the cell left. The anions, however, are mostly too large to get through the layer or "membrane" which surrounds the cell, and instead potassium ions are pulled into the cell from the solution outside. If they entered to such an extent that they exactly neutralised, electrically, the negative charges on the anions, they would immediately start leaving again. They would be in much higher concentration inside the cell than outside, and all substances in solution tend to move from a region of higher concentration to one of lower: a very slight excess of anions remains (much too small to be detected by chemical analysis), the inside of the cell is electrically negative to the outside, and the tendency of the potassium ions to move out is just equalled by the electrical attraction of their positive charges to the excess negative charges of the anions.

The potential difference between the inside of the cell and the outside solution can be measured if an extremely small tube, less than $\frac{1}{1000}$ mm. in diameter, is inserted into the cell. This procedure is one of some delicacy, and special amplifiers are necessary owing to the very high electrical resistance of the "micro-pipette". The concentration of potassium ions in the contents of a nerve fibre is about 50 times that in the solution outside, and the contents are electrically negative to the outside solution by some 50 to 100 millivolts; in these conditions, there is no net force moving the potassium ions in either direction. The concentration of sodium ions in the contents of the fibre, on the other hand, is about one-tenth of that in the outside solution: the gradient of concentration and the electrical potential difference both act in the direction of forcing sodium ions to enter the fibre, which they do, but not so rapidly that they cannot be expelled at the same rate by the "sodium pump".

This is the condition in the inactive ("resting") nerve fibre. When a nerve impulse is initiated something in the nature of a "gate" in the surface membrane is opened, allowing sodium ions to enter several hundred times as rapidly as before: the positive charges carried by them reduce and eventually reverse the "resting" potential difference, and the contents of the fibre become some 20 to 40 millivolts positive to the outside solution. (This, again, can be measured by means of a micro-pipette inserted into the fibre.) A second "gate" now opens, allowing free passage for potassium ions, which are now driven out of the fibre both by their concentration gradient and by the electrical potential difference (now reversed), and the sodium "gate" closes: the loss of potassium ions restores the potential difference to the resting, negative, value and the potassium "gate" closes. All this happens in about $\frac{1}{2000}$ second in the most rapid nerve fibres, but may take a second or more in slower kinds of excitable cell. The "sodium pump" then expels, in a more leisurely manner, the sodium ions which have come in through the "gate", allowing potassium ions to enter in exchange.

Each nerve impulse, therefore, is accompanied by a change of some 100 millivolts in the electrical potential difference between the inside and outside of the fibre. The quantity of electricity which must be transferred across the surface membrane in order to produce this change in potential difference depends on the capacitance of the membrane. This is surprisingly large, one microfarad per square centimetre, since the thickness of the membrane is about one-hundredth of the wave-length of visible light. Nevertheless, since ions carry such large electrical charges, it has been found that when an impulse travels through, say, one centimetre length of nerve fibre, the quantity of sodium ions entering, and of potassium ions leaving, is about 1 millionth of the quantity present within the fibre. It is not surprising, therefore, that electric methods are used for studying nerve impulses. That about this quantity of sodium and potassium ions do enter and leave the nerve fibre has, moreover, been confirmed by measuring the movements of their radioactive isotopes.

The passage of a nerve impulse can be detected by recording the electrical changes accompanying it, without inserting an electrode inside the fibre. In the "resting" condition, the inside is negative to the outside, and thus the outside is positive to the inside: in the "active" condition, the potential difference reverses and the outside becomes negative to the inside. Thus in the region occupied by the impulse at any moment, the outside of the fibre becomes electrically negative to the more distant regions which the impulse has left, or has not yet reached, as shown in *Figure 3*. This "action potential", or pulse of electrical change accompanying the nerve impulse, can be recorded by means of a pair of electrodes—which may consist of fine wires—placed on the outside of the nerve. It has been known and studied since the middle of the nineteenth century; but the nature of the ionic movements which give rise to it were not known until 100 years later.

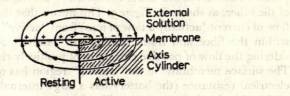

FIGURE 3 *Diagram showing the electrical potential differences across the surface membrane of a nerve fibre.*

In the "resting" condition (on the left) the inside of the fibre ("axis cylinder") is electrically negative to the outside ("external solution"). In the region where an impulse is present at any moment ("active" condition, on the right) the inside is electrically positive to the outside. In consequence there are circulating currents, as shown by the lines, positively charged ions moving in the direction shown by the arrows; these partially depolarise the membrane in the "resting" region and start up an impulse there. The impulse thus moves steadily from right to left.

(L. E. Bayliss, 1960. "Principles of General Physiology." Longmans, Green and Co. Ltd.)

As in the early types of electric telegraph, the signals are renewed at intervals along the line by feeding in power through "relays". This arises from the properties of the "gates" which allow sodium and potassium ions to enter and leave the nerve fibre. We know very little about these "gates" except that they are kept closed by the "resting" negative potential difference between the inside and the outside of the fibre. If this "membrane potential" is reduced (by passing an electric current through electrodes applied to the nerve, for example—the normal method of "stimulating" it) a critical value is reached at which the sodium "gate" begins to open: this, leads to a further reduction in the membrane potential, further opening of the "gate" and so on. The whole process "runs away", is "regenerative", and stops only when the membrane potential has been reversed and has reached a value sufficient to stop further entry of sodium ions. The nerve impulse is thus "all-or-nothing", and ordinarily one can never detect any impulses in any nerve fibre that are less than full-sized for that particular kind of fibre. Now at the junction of an "active" stretch of nerve fibre with the neighbouring "resting" stretch, we have, in effect, two batteries in series, the positive terminal of one being connected to the negative terminal of the other, as shown in *Figure 3*. This means that there will be a flow of current (actually a flow of ions) from "active" to "resting" within the fibre and from "resting" to "active" outside (considering the flow of positive current or of positively charged ions). The surface membrane in the "resting" region has quite a large electrical resistance (the battery has a large internal resistance), so that this circulating current will reduce the potential difference across it. If this "depolarisation" reaches the critical value, the regenerative action on the sodium "gate" will be started, the "relay" operated, and the "active" region will move along into the previously "resting" region. The power associated with the impulse at any point on the nerve is derived from the essentially unstable distribution of ions, maintained in the "resting" state by the action of the "sodium pump": it is quite independent of any power that may be needed to start an impulse travelling along the nerve.

In telegraph systems, relays are needed only at intervals of several hundred miles; in nerve fibres the signal strength decays very rapidly with distance along the line and the interval between relays is very short. In the "myelinated" nerve fibres which are used by vertebrates, the positions of the relays can be seen under the microscope and are about 1 mm. apart; they are known as "nodes of Ranvier" and are indicated in *Figure 2*. In the non-myelinated nerves used by invertebrates and for some purposes by vertebrates, the relays are effectively contiguous, the whole surface of the fibre being capable of relay action. In consequence of the necessity for having relays at such short intervals, the nerve impulses travel along the fibre much more slowly than do the impulses in a telegraph wire—at about 1 to 100 metres per second as against nearly 300,000 kilometres per second.

Initiation of nerve impulses. In the ordinary course of events, other than those of special experimental studies, the nerve impulses travelling down an axon originate in its nerve cell, in response to the arrival of impulses in the axons of other cells. Like an axon, the cell "fires" an impulse when the membrane potential is reduced by a certain critical amount. At the junction between the nerve endings of an axon and the next nerve cell in the chain (called a "synapse"), and at the junction between the axon endings and a muscle cell (called an "end-plate"), it has been found that this "depolarisation" results from a local and temporary removal of the restriction imposed by the surface membrane on the movements of ions through it; this applies to all kinds of ions, and is as if a hole had been made through the membrane. At some junctions between nerve endings and nerve or muscle cells, this "hole" is known to be produced by the action of a "chemical mediator" or "transmitter", released from the nerve endings by the impulses as they arrive; this may be so at all such junctions. The situation at the synapse or end-plate is now essentially similar to that at the boundary between an "active" region of a nerve fibre and a "resting" region, as shown in *Figure 3*. The battery is abolished at the "hole", not actually reversed as it is in the "active" region, but the flow of current (or ions) is exactly the same, and leads to partial depolarisation of the near-by "resting" surface membrane, opening of the sodium "gate" and the initiation of a nerve impulse. At the "hole" there is virtually direct connection between the solution outside the nerve (or muscle) cell and that inside: near the "hole", therefore, the outside solution becomes electrically negative to more distant regions. The potential difference may be measured in suitable circumstances, but it will be smaller than the true membrane potential of the cell (as measured by an electrode inside it) by an amount which depends on how close to the "hole" the electrode is placed. The change in potential at an electrode, whether inside the cell or close to the "hole" outside it, consequent on the appearance of the "hole", is called the "generator potential", since it is this which generates the nerve impulse.

Receptors. In living control systems the misalignment detectors are known as "receptors" which, according to their specific properties, convert into nerve impulses movements or forces

applied to them, changes in their temperature, or in the amount
of light falling on them. Some receptors may be "sense organs"
and their excitation may give rise to sensations, e.g. of touching
an object, of the temperature of the air, or of illumination: but
as parts of control systems it makes no difference whether there is
conscious sensation or not.

Nerve impulses are initiated at receptor cells in essentially the
same way as they are initiated at nerve cells. When a receptor
cell is stimulated by an appropriate physical or chemical change
in its surroundings, a "receptor potential" may be detected: this
may itself act as the generator potential; or in some of the more
elaborate kinds of receptor system, there may be an additional
source of power which is "modulated" by the receptor potential
and then acts as the generator potential. It is as if a thermionic
valve had been added, the receptor potential being applied to
the grid and the change in anode current used to create the
generator potential.

Adjustor action

In all but the simplest kinds of servo system, signals from
several different measuring devices converging on the misalignment element and often, also, on the input and output elements,
are added together, subtracted from each other and perhaps
modified in various other ways. In animals, many of these mathematical operations are performed at the junctions between one
nerve cell and the next.

The arrival of a single impulse in a single axon at its synapse on
a nerve cell (or on one of the fine processes called "dendrites"
which stick out all round it) may not produce a generator potential
of sufficient size to "fire" the cell. The generator potential, however, lasts much longer than the nerve impulse, and is not "all-
or-nothing". The cell may fire, therefore, if enough impulses
arrive sufficiently rapidly for their generator potentials to
combine and reach the critical size: they may arrive in succession
along a single axon ("temporal summation"), or nearly simultaneously along several different axons ("spatial summation").
Since these axons may be derived from different nerve cells,
spatial summation provides a means for adding together the
signals from many different receptor cells. Some of the junctions,
moreover, may be "inhibitory": a "hole" is not made in the
surface membrane, but a potassium "gate" is opened widely,

probably by means of a special kind of chemical transmitter: it then becomes more difficult for "excitatory" synapses to start an impulse, since any reduction in the membrane potential produced by an influx of sodium ions at these synapses is immediately countered by an outflux of potassium ions at the open "gate". Impulses arriving at inhibitory synapses are thus, in effect, subtracted from those arriving at excitatory synapses. The mathematical operations produced by the presence of temporal summation will be discussed later.

Effectors

The "motors" of living control systems, or "effectors" as they are usually called, are: (1) muscle cells of various kinds; (2) cells which manufacture and "secrete" various chemical substances either into the alimentary canal of an animal, for example, (external secretion), or into the blood stream or other "extra-cellular fluid" (internal secretion); and (3) cells which transport substances already present into or out of the body fluids from or to the outside world, or from one part of the body fluids to another. Plants, of course, have no muscle cells, but their "effectors" probably work in much the same way as do the secreting and transporting cells in animals.

Nerve impulses travelling to the muscle cells in the fibres of the "motor nerves" produce generator potentials which are here called "end-plate potentials". At some of the end-plates in some invertebrates—crustaceans and insects in particular—there may be spatial and temporal summation, as at the synapses in the nervous system. It is not certain that secreting and transporting cells are excited by means of generator potentials, but it is known that their activities may be increased or decreased either by chemical transmitters, released at the endings of the "secretory nerves", or by hormones reaching them from the blood stream, which have much the same action.

It is a peculiarity of all kinds of "motor" in living control systems that in general they will work only in one direction; with perhaps a few exceptions, they cannot be reversed. A muscle, for example, can pull but it cannot push, so that our limbs are moved in one direction by one set of muscles and in the other direction by a different set. There is, indeed, no provision in the nervous system "code" for distinguishing between "positive" and "negative" signals except by using different nerve fibres. There are both excitatory and inhibitory hormones, but the latter are not strictly "negative" in the sense that they reverse the action of the effectors; they merely reduce or prevent it. The receptors, however, may be "biased" and set up a steady stream of impulses at the set-point of the system, the frequency being increased or decreased according to the sign of the misalignment. These features do not introduce any particular complications into the system—similar features, indeed, may be found in non-living systems. But in some of the processes concerned in homeostasis the system controlling departures from the normal state in one direction may be entirely different from that controlling departures in the opposite direction; and this does complicate matters.

The terms "receptor", "adjustor" and "effector" were introduced by the American biologist G. H. Parker in 1911 as a result of his studies on the "elementary" nervous systems in simple and primitive animals. No one at that time realised how well these terms would fit in with the essential features of control systems as developed by engineers. For convenience in representation and analysis, all the adjustor actions, which modify the misalignment signal are lumped together in the controller. But in practical systems, both living and non-living, the signal may be (and usually is) modified both in the misalignment detectors (receptors) and in the motors (effectors) in consequence of their inherent properties. We shall discuss this in more detail later.

3 ELEMENTARY PROPERTIES OF SERVO SYSTEMS. RESPONSES TO SUDDEN CHANGES OF INPUT

When the input to a servo system is changed in any way, the output will change also, but not in general in precisely the same way. (a) If the system is left undisturbed after the change in input, there may be a residual difference between output and input, or "steady state error". (b) There will be a "transient period" before the output has reached some arbitrary (and acceptably small) distance from the steady state. (c) The output may oscillate: if this occurs, the rate at which the oscillations die away will determine the duration of the transient period; if they do not die away at all, the system is "unstable", and in general useless. (Some non-linear systems, however, are essentially unstable, but quite useful, as will appear in Chapter 7.) The size of the steady state error, the duration of the transient period and the possibility that oscillation will occur, all depend upon the properties of the components present in the system.

The diagram given in *Figure 1* (p. 6) shows a "load" attached to the output element; if there were no load, there would be little point in having a servo system at all, since the small force needed to move the input element could equally well move the output element directly. The force exerted by this load (which must be moved by the motor) will in general vary with the position of the output element, the speed with which it is moving, or both. We assume that the motor develops a force which is proportional to the signal sent to it from the controller: if it works on compressed air, for example, the force will be proportional to the air pressure delivered to it; if it is an electric motor, the force will be proportional to the voltage across its terminals. The signal from the controller, however, will depend on the misalignment, the rate of change of the misalignment, the rate of change of the output, and on various other factors according to the type of control considered.

B

Proportional control

The controller generates a signal which is proportional to the misalignment at any moment, the constant of proportionality being known as the "stiffness" of the system; this, alternatively, is the "gain" in the controller—i.e. the change in size of the signal as it passes through—multiplied by the constant which relates the force exerted by the motor to the signal applied to it.

Steady state errors. Suppose that the load were a spring which had to be compressed by the motor. This cannot be done unless the motor receives power from the controller, which happens only when there is a misalignment. The motor, therefore, will be unable to move the output element through exactly the same distance as the input element is moved. When the system has come to rest there will be a steady state error, which increases with increase in the departure of the output element from its initial position. Similarly, in a system controlling the flow of heat or water, the "load" is likely to increase with increase in the rate of flow, for example as a result of viscous friction in the pipes. There will again be a steady state error, unless the flow through the system is zero; since it increases with increase in the velocity given to the output element, it is known as a "steady state velocity error". For a given load, the steady state errors can be reduced by adjusting the controller so as to increase the force exerted by the motor in response to a given amount of misalignment—i.e. by increasing the stiffness, or the gain, of the system; but it can never be reduced to zero. With the simplest kind of servo system, homeostasis can never be perfect.

The same effect may be produced by the inherent properties of the motor. Several kinds of electric motor, for example, exert a maximum twisting force ("torque") on the shaft when they are stationary, and a progressively smaller torque as they speed up. This is not due only to the presence of friction in the bearings; the faster the electric motor runs, for example, the less current does it draw from the mains. Formally, however, the effect is exactly the same as if there were a frictional load, as will be brought out more clearly later (p. 158), and there will be a steady state velocity error even if the output load is independent of the speed of movement. In living systems, muscles of all kinds exert a smaller force as the speed of movement increases. We all know that we can lift a cricket ball rapidly, but a cannon ball only slowly. The same probably applies to secreting and transporting cells, but the evidence is less certain. This will be discussed more fully in Chapter 6.

There are several kinds of animal which live in estuaries and on the sea shore—notably crustaceans (crabs and crayfish for example) and worms of various kinds. When the tide is in, they are immersed in sea water; when the tide is out, they are likely to find themselves in mixtures of sea water and fresh water of varying concentration according to the amount of water coming down the river or the amount of rain falling on the shore. Most of these animals possess what is known as "osmotic regulation" and maintain the concentration of their body fluids more or less constant in spite of the fluctuations in the water outside them. There is a polychaete worm *Nereis diversicolor* whose osmotic control system appears to be of a simple and not very effective kind. When suddenly transferred from sea water to water which is half sea water and half fresh water, its body fluids become equivalent, not to 50 per cent sea water, but to 55 per cent sea water, as shown in *Figure 4*. If transferred to one-quarter sea water and three-quarters fresh water, its body fluids become equivalent to 40 per cent sea water, instead of 25 per cent. The animal would appear to be "trying" to be free and independent as far as the concentration of its body fluids is concerned, but is

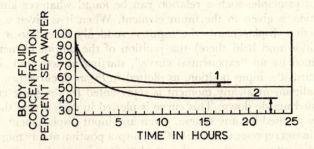

FIGURE 4   *Osmotic control in the worm* Nereis diversicolor

At time 0, some worms were put in sea water diluted to one-half (curve 1) and others into sea water diluted to one-quarter (curve 2), and the concentration of their body fluids measured at intervals. The worms maintained their concentrations at 55 per cent sea water (curve 1) and at 40 per cent sea water (curve 2) respectively.

(L. E. Bayliss, 1960. "Principles of General Physiology." Longmans, Green and Co. Ltd. Original from L. C. Beadle, 1937.)

not very successful. The more dilute the outside water, the harder must the control system work in order to keep up the concentration of its body fluids: there is a steady state error equivalent to 45 per cent sea water when the animal is in 50 per cent sea water, and to 60 per cent sea water when it is in 25 per cent sea water.

Transient responses. If the input element is given a sudden very rapid displacement, the motor will exert a force depending on the amount of misalignment produced. As the output element catches up on the input element, and the misalignment becomes smaller, the motor will exert a progressively smaller force. In a simple system with viscous friction, the velocity of the output element at any moment must be such that the frictional force opposing the motor (proportional to the output velocity) is just equal to the force exerted by the motor (proportional to the misalignment at that moment). If it were not, there would be a residual force tending to increase or decrease the velocity. The loop transfer function of the system, accordingly, defines a relation between the output *velocity* and the misalignment, with stiffness and coefficient of friction as constants. By means of the mathematical process of integration, a relation may be derived between output *position*, misalignment and time: since misalignment is (input)–(output), this provides, also, a relation between output, input and time, and thus a concise description of the behaviour of the system.

In principle, such a relation can be found whatever kind of motion is given to the input element. When it is given a step function displacement (the input is suddenly moved to a new position and held there) the position of the output element is defined by an "exponential curve", starting at zero and rising towards the input position, as plotted in *Figure 8*, curve (*a*). The misalignment at any moment is represented by the same curve turned upside down. This curve is plotted in such a way that it may be used for any system, given any input displacement. The ordinates represent the ratio of the output position at any moment to the output position in the steady state—i.e. to the new input position *minus* the steady state error introduced by an "elastic" load, if any. (The diagram is drawn for a system without steady state error.) The abscissae represent the ratio of time (in seconds, for example) to the "time constant" of the system (also in seconds) —i.e. the time constant is used as unit of time. This constant, defined as the time taken for the misalignment to fall to 37 per cent of its initial value (it falls to 5 per cent of the initial value in 3 time constants) is proportional to the frictional coefficients of the load (or the coefficient defining the force–velocity relation of the motor), and is inversely proportional to the stiffness of the system, or the gain in the controller. For a given kind of motor and load, therefore, the performance of the system in respect of accuracy and speed is improved by increasing the gain. But in practice, as we shall see, there are limits to the amount of gain that can be used.

Floating control

The steady state velocity error can be reduced, or eliminated altogether, in one of two ways which are of interest in connection with living control systems. The first, much used by engineers when designing control systems, is to insert a device in the controller which "remembers" all the misalignment that has occurred in the past and activates the motor in proportion to all this past misalignment as well as in proportion to any misalignment present at the moment. There can be no steady state error, since if there were, the activation of the motor would steadily increase until it vanished. It is not difficult to see that the addition of such *"integral control"* (the misalignment being integrated, in the mathematical sense, with respect to time) is likely to cause the output element to overshoot the position of zero instantaneous misalignment so that it has to be brought back again by reversal of the motor. The way in which such oscillations are kept within bounds, and not allowed to continue indefinitely, will be discussed later.

The second method of reducing the steady state velocity error is to feed into the controller a signal which is proportional to the rate of the *input* to the system: the motor thus receives power from the controller even when the misalignment is zero. This is known as *input feed forward*. It is an "open loop" method of control, independent of the misalignment and the "closed loop" formed by feedback from the output of the system. If the steady state error is to be reduced to zero, the fraction of the input rate fed to the controller must be adjusted according to the amount of viscous friction (or other "load") on the output element. This may not be exactly known, and may vary according to circumstances; even when the system is set up as accurately as possible, the steady state error is likely to vary about zero, sometimes positive and sometimes negative.

In living control systems, input feed forward is not uncommon: it may be present, for example, in the "osmotic" control system of the worm *Nereis diversicolor*, already mentioned. When a steady state has been reached in diluted sea water, the worm will be losing salt at a rate which, at least as a first approximation, is proportional to the difference between the concentration of its body fluids and the concentration of the water in which it is immersed: this is the "input" to the control system. The salt-transporting cells (the "motors" of the control system) must be pumping salt into the animal (the "output" of the system) at the same rate. The misalignment is the departure of the salt content of the animal from the "set-point" which, on the simplest view, is the content when the animal is in normal sea water: the misalignment is thus proportional to the difference between the concentration of sea water and the concentration of the body fluids of the animals when in diluted sea water. (Changes in the water content of the animal may be neglected for the present purposes.) In the simplest "ideal" system (from the point of view of the mathematician) the steady state misalignment (written as θ_s) will be directly proportional to the input rate (written as u), as is demonstrated formally in Chapter 8 (p. 152). From *Figure 4* we see that when the animal was in 50 per cent sea water, $u = (55 - 50) = 5$, and $\theta_s = (100 - 55) = 45$ (using percentage sea water as arbitrary units). When the animal was in 25 per cent sea water, $u = (40 - 25) = 15$, a threefold increase, but $\theta_s = (100 - 40) = 60$, an increase of only one-third. The salt-transporting cells were activated more than in proportion to the increase in the misalignment signal (from receptors sensitive to changes in the concentration of the animal's body fluids): the response of the receptors may have been non-linear, but there may have been, in addition, signals from receptors sensitive to changes in the concentration of the external sea water, which provided an input feed forward.

Integral control does not seem to be used in living systems except in a very limited way. The responses of some kinds of receptor depend upon the product of the intensity of the exciting stimulus and the time during which it is applied—or to the time integral of the stimulus if the intensity is not constant. In those sensitive to light, for example, there is a photochemical reaction which proceeds, or "advances" steadily while light is falling on the receptor. (A photochemical reaction occurs, also, in a photographic emulsion, and it is common knowledge that a reduction in light intensity can be compensated by an increase in exposure time.) But in most of the light-sensitive receptors there is also a reverse "dark" reaction, increasing in rate as the products of the "forward" photochemical reaction increase in concentration; and eventually a steady state is reached and no further integration occurs. In a man's eyes this happens after an interval of only about $\frac{1}{10}$ second. Again, in the presence of a certain misalignment, a gland of internal secretion which forms a link in the controller will release its hormone at a rate depending on the frequency of nerve impulses reaching it, and thus on the magnitude of the misalignment. The concentration of the hormone in the

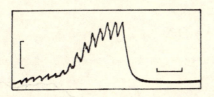

FIGURE 5   *End-plate Potentials in one of the muscles which open the claw of a crayfish*

The motor nerve was stimulated at a frequency of 135 per second: each upward kick on the record represents an end-plate potential; they increase progressively in size, and each is added to the residue of the previous one.

The vertical and horizontal bars are calibration marks and represent 1.5 millivolts and 25 milliseconds, respectively.

(L. E. Bayliss, 1960. "Principles of General Physiology." Longmans, Green and Co. Ltd. Original from B. Katz and S. W. Kuffler, 1946, Proceedings of the Royal Society, Vol. B 133.)

blood, and thus the magnitude of the effect on the "target organ" (which may be the "motor" of the servo system) will thus build up gradually: the action of the misalignment on the motor will be integrated with respect to time. But all the hormones studied so far disappear, or become inactivated, spontaneously; they are not removed or antagonised solely by a reversal of the misalignment. If the rate of secretion is constant, the concentration in the blood will eventually reach a value at which the rate of disappearance is equal to the rate of secretion, there will be no further change in the concentration and no more integral control.

This will probably occur within minutes, or perhaps hours, although few of these systems have been fully studied.

The existence of temporal summation in the nervous system may introduce a similar limited type of integral control. *Figure 5* shows how the end-plate potential at the muscle which opens the claw of a crayfish increases progressively as a series of impulses comes down the motor nerve. In this particular muscle the size of the contraction is proportional to the size of the end-plate potential, and thus depends, up to a point, on the time integral of the

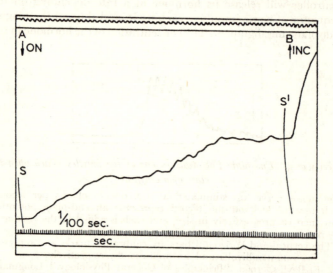

FIGURE 6   *Temporal Summation in the Nervous System of a Dog*

Only that part of the nervous system which lies in the spinal cord was functioning, the rest having been put out of action. The skin over one toe was stimulated electrically about 45 times per second, as shown by the zig-zag line at the top of the diagram. This, like stepping on a nail, caused the leg to be withdrawn reflexly, and the contraction of one of the muscles concerned was recorded by a lever attached to it and writing on a moving paper. The line in the middle of the diagram shows how the contraction gradually increased as successive nerve impulses arrived at the nervous system.

A and *S* mark the beginning of the excitation: at *B* and S^1 the strength of the electrical stimulation was suddenly increased and a greater number of receptors excited (spatial summation).

(C. S. Sherrington, 1947. "The Integrative Action of the Nervous System." Cambridge University Press).

excitation. A limiting size is reached, however, since the end-plate potential (like all generator potentials) begins to disappear again as soon as it is created by a nerve impulse, as is shown on the record. This kind of integration will not occur generally at synapses in the nervous system (or at the end-plates of most kinds of muscle), since when a nerve cell fires, the generator potential vanishes and has to be built up again from the beginning. But suppose we have a single nerve fibre carrying impulses from a receptor cell which is detecting the misalignment in the control system. This usually divides and sends its impulses to a number of nerve cells which, we will suppose, fire only after the arrival of 1, 2, 3, 4 etc. impulses from the receptor. Each of these cells sends an axon to, say, one of the many muscle fibres which make up a whole muscle. If a steady stream of impulses comes in from the receptor (there is a constant misalignment) the muscle fibres will be excited one after the other, and the contraction of the muscle will become progressively greater. The various alternative paths through the nervous system, requiring different amounts of temporal summation, may each contain several nerve cells in series, with a corresponding increase in the total time over which summation occurs. This may be up to a second or so in, say, a dog, as shown in *Figure 6*, instead of the few hundredths of a second which is the duration of the generator potential.

Some integral control results, also, from the properties of the contractile part of the muscle fibres themselves. On excitation by a nerve impulse the muscle cell becomes "activated", shortens and develops tension: but the development of tension, and the subsequent "relaxation", are relatively slow, and activation ceases before the tension has built up to its maximum possible value. If a second nerve impulse arrives after a sufficiently short interval, the activation is renewed before the tension developed in response to the first impulse has disappeared: the second contraction is superposed on the first. Thus the tension will increase progressively as successive nerve impulses arrive.

These effects are particularly well shown in sea anemones. As may easily be observed in a suitable pool on the sea shore, a sea anemone with all its tentacles showing protects itself when prodded by withdrawing the tentacles and closing the entrance to its body cavity by contraction of a ring of mucles fibres known as the "sphincter", like tying a string round the opening of a sack. If, in a laboratory, we use electrical stimulation, which is more

E *

accurately controlled than mechanical prodding, we find that
there is no detectable response to the first one (or perhaps two)
electric shocks of a regular series, however strong they are, short
of injuring the animal (*Figure 7 (b)* and *(d)*). Subsequently, the

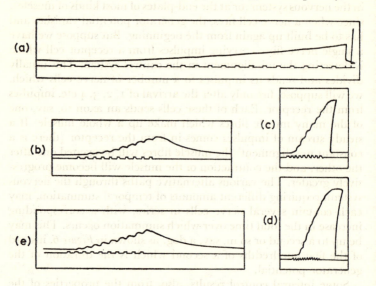

FIGURE 7   *Summation of excitation and contraction in the sphincter*
of the sea anemone Calliactis.

A series of electric shocks was applied to the base of the animal close
to its attachment to the ground, and the contractions of the marginal
sphincter, which closes the top of the animal over the tentacles, were
recorded on a moving paper.

In (*a*), (*b*), (*c*) and (*d*) the stimulus was just strong enough to give a
response. The frequency of stimulation was: (*a*) 1 every 1.69 sec.; (*b*) 1
every 1 sec.; (*c*) 1 every 0.5 sec.; (*d*) 1 every 0.28 sec. The height of the
contraction increases with the frequency of excitation.

In (*e*) the stimulus was 15 times greater than the threshold, at a frequency of 1 every 1 sec. Comparison of (*b*) with (*e*) shows that the height
of the contraction did not depend on the strength of the excitation.

sphincter shortens in a series of steps, at first small, then larger, as
shown in *Figure 7*. Each contraction is built on the remains of the
previous one, and is larger the more frequent are the stimuli. The
smaller is the interval between the nerve impulses, the more do
they summate at the nerve-muscle junctions; the excitation pene-

trates the less sensitive junctions and more muscle fibres contract. The sea anemone, in fact, can control the contraction of its sphincter only by making use of these summation effects. The nervous system (in the form of a "nerve net") acts as a single unit giving "all-or-nothing" responses, as shown by the fact that the contractions of the sphincter do not increase if the strength of the electric shock is increased. The receptor cells on its surface, sensitive to mechanical stimulation, set up a succession of nerve impulses when the animal is prodded, the duration and frequency depending on the duration and vigour of the prodding.

All these summation effects in the nervous system and the muscles, like that due to a hormonal link, are limited in duration. They will reduce a steady state velocity error only if the disturbances to which the control system is responding are so rapid that they are completed before the end of the summation period. It is doubtful whether this should properly be regarded as integral control at all.

Oscillation or "hunting"

If a servo system contains elements with *inertia*, or if there is a *delay* in the transmission of the signals at one or more points in the closed loop, the output is likely to oscillate, or "hunt" about the steady state value. There is no harm in a certain amount of hunting, provided that it does not go on for too long—i.e. provided that the amplitude of the oscillations dies away to a negligible value after a few swings in each direction.

Inertia. This is more important to engineers than to biologists. Nearly all mechanical systems possess significant amounts of inertia, either in the load which is driven or in the motor which drives it: whereas in living systems, inertia is likely to be important only in the control of the movement of the limbs of the larger and more active animals. If the output element (motor and load) possesses inertia, it will go on moving after the misalignment has become zero and activation of the motor has ceased. A reversed misalignment will be created, and this will be corrected by reversed activation of the motor; the output element will overshoot again, and so on.

The existence of *delays* will have a very similar effect. Suppose, for example, that the misalignment signal is delayed on its way through the controller: activation of the motor will not cease when the misalignment is zero, but a short time later; the output element will overshoot and generate a reversed misalignment, just as happens when there is inertia. The same effect will be produced by a delay between the output element and the misalignment detector, or in the detector itself. Indeed, nearly all the devices used by engineers for measuring the misalignment possess appreciable delay—notably thermometers and other temperature-sensitive instruments.

Delays are present in almost all living control systems. In the nervous system the nerve impulses may take a few thousandths of a second up to a few tenths of a second to travel from one end of the axon to the other: at every junction between an axon and the next nerve cell in the chain or the muscle or secreting cell which is acting as a motor, there is a delay before the generator potential reaches the critical size (particularly if much temporal summation is needed) or before the muscle or secreting cell has responded to the excitation; it may be only a few thousandths of a second in the quick-moving warm-blooded vertebrates, but may reach several seconds in more sluggish animals. Lastly, if in any part of the loop the signal is carried in the blood stream of the animal, either by some hormone or by the controlled quantity itself, there will be a delay since the blood takes time to flow from one point to another. In ourselves, for example, it takes about 10 seconds for such a signal to be carried in the blood from our feet to our brains.

Although these delays may seem very small in the nervous systems of warm-blooded animals (in which control systems have been most studied) they may add up to significant values. The interval between the moment when the driver of a motor car sees an obstruction and the moment when he applies the brake may be about ¼ second, during which time, if his speed were 60 miles per hour, he would travel 22 feet. The presence of such "reaction times", also, has been shown to affect the accuracy of mechanical homeostatic systems (such as keeping a gun pointed at a moving target) in which a human operator acts as a link between the misalignment detector and the controller.

All the delays so far mentioned are known as "*finite delays*", or "dead times": a signal applied suddenly to one end of the link will appear equally suddenly at the other end after a definite period of time, as is shown graphically in *Figure 8* (*c*). There are also "*exponential delays*" whose properties may perhaps be best seen in an example. Suppose a man suddenly moves one of his legs. The active muscles generate heat, get warmer and warm the blood flowing through them: this warm blood will eventually reach the brain where there are receptors sensitive to changes in temperature which are important in the control system for temperature regulation; these, therefore, will be excited after a finite delay. But there are other receptors sensitive to temperature which are in the skin overlying the muscles: heat will be conducted to them through the tissues and body fluids which lie between mucles and skin. Now the rate at which heat is conducted from muscles to receptors depends on the difference in temperature between them. If the temperature of the muscles rises rapidly and then stays constant, the temperature difference is large to begin with,

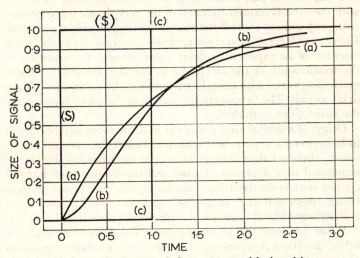

FIGURE 8   *Responses of components with time delays*

At time 0, the excitatory stimulus rises suddenly from 0 to 1, as shown by line(s). The time course of the responses are shown by lines (*a*), (*b*) and (*c*).

Curve (a): component with a simple exponential delay with a time constant 1.0.

Curve (b): component with two simple exponential delays in series, each with a time constant 0.5.

Curve (c): component with a finite delay with delay time 1.0.

The diagram shows also how the output of a servo system varies with time when the input is given a sudden displacement.

Curve (a): system with proportional control and viscous friction on the output element (or negative output velocity feedback).

Curve (b): the same system with, in addition, an exponential delay, or inertia on the output element, the damping being "critical".

and the temperature of the receptors begins to rise rapidly: and then, as the receptors warm up, the temperature difference becomes smaller and smaller, the temperature of the receptors rises more and more slowly, and in theory will never reach precisely that of the muscles. An exactly similar kind of delay would occur if, instead of the conduction of heat, we considered the diffusion of some chemical substance to which the receptors were sensitive, as occurs in many living control systems.

The transfer function of an exponential delay states that the rate of change (velocity) of the response at any moment is proportional to the difference ("misalignment") between stimulus and response at that moment. It is identical in form, therefore, with the overall transfer function of the very simple servo system, with proportional control and viscous friction, already considered. Curve (a) of *Figure 8*, therefore, shows also how the ratio of the response of an exponential delay (proportional, for example, to the temperature of the receptors) to the step function stimulus given to it, varies with time, in terms of the "time constant" of the delay as unit. The "exponential" nature of the curve accounts for the name given to the delay.

Delays of a similar kind will occur in the nervous and hormonal links between receptors and effectors, and at the effectors themselves, whenever the effects produced by the incoming signals are summated over a period of time. All the examples of integral control previously described may be equally well—and perhaps better—described as examples of exponential delays (possibly of a complicated kind) combined with amplification of the signal.

When there are two or more exponential delays, one after the other, the curve representing the response to a sudden excitation changes its shape and becomes S-shaped, as shown in curve (b), *Figure 8*. The more delays there are, the more closely does the response curve approximate to that of a finite delay.

One other type of delay may be mentioned, since it may occur in living systems and complicate the analysis. A *complex exponential delay* is introduced by a measuring device which contains inertia, such as a liquid manometer measuring pressures, or a small dynamo (tachogenerator) measuring velocities in terms of the voltage produced. If such an instrument is given a sudden stimulus, the indication, or response, will not immediately start to change at a certain rate, and then slow down gradually, as it would if it had a simple exponential delay; the rate of change of the response will increase gradually to a maximum value and then decrease again. Unless properly designed, a device of this kind may oscillate: if it just fails to oscillate, the response to a sudden excitation follows the same time course as does that of a device with two equal independent simple exponential delays in succession (*Figure 8*, curve (*b*)).

In living systems, receptors are unlikely to possess inertia, but some have been observed to show temporal summation and thus to have an integrating action. If, for example, the difference between stimulus and response were held constant, the response would not increase at a constant rate, but at a progressively increasing rate: the transfer function will include a term proportional to acceleration, as does that for a complex exponential delay with inertia.

Damping

Any tendency of a servo system to oscillate, whether due to the addition of integral control or to the presence of inertia or time delays, can be checked by introducing a force, opposing the movement of the output element, which is proportional to the speed at which it is moving: such a force is said to introduce "damping" into the system. It may be due to viscous friction, such as would be introduced by a suitable form of hydraulic or electromagnetic brake (a pendulum will not swing if its bob is immersed in treacle); but this absorbs power from the motor and is thus inefficient. Alternatively, a signal proportional to the velocity of the output element may be fed into the controller in such a way that it opposes the signal proportional to the misalignment (*negative output velocity feedback*) : the automatic reduction in force, or torque, exerted by the motor as its speed increases is due, in effect, to the motor introducing output velocity feedback into itself. But the use of output velocity feedback introduces a steady state velocity error, just as does that of friction in the load. We may arrange the feedback link so that the output velocity signal reaches the controller only when the velocity is changing, and is blocked when the velocity is constant, after the steady state has been reached ("transient output velocity feedback"); the damping is present when it is needed, but absent when it would introduce a steady state error.

Error rate control. It is better, however, to put the damping on the misalignment. In the steady state, the misalignment is ideally zero, or if not, it is constant: in either event the rate of change of misalignment is zero and the damping force vanishes. What in fact is usually done is to add to the signal proportional to the misalignment, which is fed to the controller, a further signal which is proportional to the rate of change of the misalignment—an "error rate" signal, as it is called.

Suppose our servo system is in a steady state with the input element moving slowly (there is, say, a slow flow of heat or water through it). The output element is moving at the same rate, and there is a small steady state error. We now increase the rate of the input: the misalignment immediately begins to increase and the motor will speed up until the output element is moving at the same increased speed, though lagging rather more behind the input element (the steady state error is greater). If there is a time delay, however, the motor will be running too fast when the steady state condition is first reached, since it is being activated by the somewhat greater misalignment which existed a short time previously. Addition of an error rate signal will check this: the misalignment is becoming smaller (its rate of change is negative) as the steady state is being approached so that the error rate signal is negative and opposes the misalignment signal itself. Thus, if the system is properly adjusted, the motor does not receive any excessive activation as the steady state condition is approached, and there is no overshoot. Conversely, during the delay before the misalignment signal reaches the motor, the misalignment will be increasing and the error rate signal will be positive: the output element will get an additional boost and catch up on the input element more rapidly. Inertia and time delays in a servo system make the responses of the output element lag behind the changes in the misalignment: the error rate signals, on the other hand, are in advance of the changes in the misalignment and thus reduce or eliminate the lag. It is not always possible, however, to make a system which hunts severely, or is actually unstable, acceptable by the use of error rate control alone, particularly if the instability is due to the presence of a finite delay. We shall return to this in the next chapter.

Error rate signals are likely to be present in all living control systems, and are introduced by the receptors which generate the misalignment signals. We can demonstrate this experimentally by recording electrically the nerve impulses in the fibres coming from suitable receptor cells. For example, all muscles contain, among the muscle fibres, receptor cells which respond to changes in the length of the muscle (these are important in the control of muscular movement, as will be discussed in Chapter 7). If we stretch the muscle by pulling on its ends, we can record nerve impulses travelling away from the muscle: there is an initial burst of impulses, after which the rate of firing settles down to a steady value which depends on the *amount* of stretch. In the initial burst, however, the rate of firing depends on the *rate* at which the muscle is stretched, as shown in *Figure 9*. Some receptors fire only in response to changes in their stimuli and are described as "rapidly adapting" receptors: but most behave like the one illustrated in *Figure 9*, giving a steady response to a steady stimulus, with an

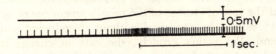

FIGURE 9 *Discharge of nerve impulses from a stretch receptor in the gastrocnemius muscle of a cat.*

The cat was "decerebrate"—i.e. the brain and all the "higher" parts of the nervous system had been removed.

The *upper line* records the length of the muscle, and the upward movement indicates when the muscle was stretched.

The *lower line* records the electrical changes accompanying the nerve impulses. Note that their *size* is constant ("all-or-nothing") but that the *frequency* becomes greater: (*a*) in the steady state when the length of the muscle is increased; and (*b*) in the transient conditions, depending on the rate of stretch.

(P. B. C. Matthews and G. Rushworth, 1958. Journal of Physiology vol. 140.)

additional response when the stimulus changes. Conversely, if we allow the muscle to shorten again, the impulses may disappear altogether for a short time and then reappear at a smaller rate corresponding to the new length: initially the effect due to the rate of change (now negative) opposes that due to the actual length at any moment. Some very rapidly adapting receptors, however, which fire only once, or perhaps three or four times, when a maintained stimulus is suddenly applied, and then remain "silent", fire again a few times when the stimulus is removed. Rapid adaptation, and sensitivity to the rate of change of the stimulus, is found in all kinds of receptor, whatever their "mod-ality", the kind of stimulus—movement, heat, light etc.—to which they are sensitive. In all those kinds so far studied, it results from a rapid disappearance of the receptor potential: it is thus due to some property of the processes by which the physical or chemical change which acts as the stimulus gives rise to the receptor potential. We know very little about these processes.

Quite apart from any such rather elaborate physiological experiments, our own sensations tell us how much more sensitive we may be to a changing stimulus than to a constant one. We move our fingers over an object in order to discover how rough is its surface: we may suddenly "see" an object (or more strictly, become aware of it) only when it moves.

The use of error rate control in practice is complicated by the fact that the rate of change of the misalignment (or of any other quantity) cannot be measured without introducing a delay of some kind. Put rather crudely, the rate of change must be measured in terms of the amount of change in some definite interval of time, and consequently, it is not known until the end of this interval. This must, presumably, apply also to the rate measuring systems provided by the rapidly adapting receptors. The transfer functions of these will be considered in more detail in later chapters.

The performance of servo systems with integral control, inertia or exponential delays.

As already remarked, the addition of integral control, the presence of inertia in the output load, or a delay in the trans-mission of the signal round the servo loop, is liable to make the system oscillate. The loop transfer functions of all these systems are formally identical (if the delay is of the simple exponential kind, and there is only one), and it is not difficult to discover by mathematical methods how the output varies with time during the transient period following a step function displacement or velocity given to the input. If there are several delays in succession, or if there is integral control, or inertia, as well as an exponential delay, the analysis becomes more complicated and difficult; if there is a finite delay, exact mathematical treatment is impossible, but graphical methods may be used if the servo system is other-wise a simple one.

Whether the system will oscillate, and if so, whether the oscillations will die away and the system merely hunt, or build up progressively so that the system is unstable, depends on the *damping coefficient*. This depends not only on the amount of viscous friction in the load, or the amount of output velocity or error rate control which is added, but also on the gain or stiffness of the system and the amount of integral control, inertia or delay. The *frequency* of the oscillations also depends on all these quantities. Thus, for example, a system with an exponential delay can be made to hunt by increasing the gain in the controller, or the time constant of the delay, as well as by decreasing the amount of output velocity feedback: increasing the gain increases the frequency of the oscillations, whereas increasing the delay decreases it.

If the damping coefficient is less than 1, the system will oscillate; and the smaller it is, the more slowly will the oscillations die away. If it is less than 0 (i.e. is negative), the oscillations will build up and the system will be unstable: this could happen, for example, if the output velocity feedback were made positive, assisting the misalignment instead of negative, opposing it; it may occur, also, when there is a finite delay in the system, and in systems which

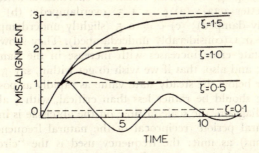

FIGURE 10 *Showing how the misalignment of a servo system which is capable of oscillation varies with time after the input is suddenly given a constant velocity*

The four lines are for different values of the damping coefficient (ζ), from above downwards: over-damped; critically damped; slightly under-damped; and considerably under-damped. The broken lines show the value of the steady state error.

The natural frequency of the system is ω_n: the time scale is in units of ($1/\omega_n$) so that one cycle is complete in 2π of these units. The misalignment scale is in terms of the product of the input velocity (u) and the natural period ($1/\omega_n$).

are more complicated than those discussed. When the damping coefficient is exactly 1, the misalignment (or output position) just fails to overshoot the steady state value even once, and the system is said to be "critically damped". The curve defining the position of the output at any moment after a step function displacement is given to the input is shown in *Figure 8* as curve (*b*): mathematically, the overall transfer function for a critically damped system with, say proportional control and an exponential delay, is identical with the transfer function of two exponential delays, with the same time constant, in series. If the damping coefficient is greater than 1, the system is "over-damped" and becomes increasingly sluggish the larger is the damping coefficient.

In *Figure 10* are plotted curves showing how the misalignment varies with time after the system, supposed initially to be at rest, is given a constant input velocity (ramp function input). The system has proportional control, with inertia or an exponential delay, and damping is on the output only (there is no integral control or error rate damping): there will thus be a steady state error. The four lines in *Figure 10* show how the misalignment varies with time when the system has one of four different values of the damping coefficient, which for shortness is written ζ (the Greek letter zeta): (a) $\zeta = 1.5$ (overdamped); (b) $\zeta = 1.0$ (critically damped); (c) $\zeta = 0.5$ (slightly underdamped); and (d) $\zeta = 0.1$ (considerably underdamped). They show how the steady state error increases with increase in the damping coefficient; and also, that if we wish to get within, say 5 per cent above or below the steady state value as rapidly as possible, the damping should be rather less than critical, with ζ about 0.5. In this diagram, the scale of time on the abscissae is in terms of the natural period (reciprocal of the natural frequency of the oscillations) as unit: the frequency used is the "circular frequency", written ω (the Greek letter omega)—i.e. the frequency in cycles per unit of time multiplied by 2π: on this scale one complete cycle occupies 2π (6.28) units of time. The steady state error will depend on the magnitude of the input velocity, and, for a given value of the damping coefficient, also on the natural frequency of the system (as is demonstrated in Chapter 8, p. 162): the misalignment scale, on the ordinates, is thus written in terms of the input velocity as unit, but this is calculated in terms of the natural period as unit of time. The object of this rather elaborate procedure is to make the scales "dimensionless", so that the same

diagram can be used, whatever input velocity is given and whatever natural frequency of oscillation the system possesses.

Phase-plane trajectories. The curves in *Figure 10* may also be
plotted in a more concise form. As may be seen from these curves,
when the system oscillates, the misalignment has alternately a
maximum displacement and a maximum velocity (maximum
slope of the curve). Similarly, a freely swinging pendulum has
zero velocity at each end of its swing, when the displacement is
maximum, and a maximum velocity each time it passes through
the middle of the swing, when its displacement is zero. If, therefore,
we plot the misalignment of the system at any moment, as
abscissae, against the rate of change (velocity) of misalignment
at the same moment, as ordinates, and the amplitude of the
oscillations is constant, we get an ellipse; by suitable choice of
scales, this may be made into a circle (see *Figure 28*, p. 98). If the
amplitude is slowly falling, the circle becomes a spiral, and the
damping coefficient may be readily observed from the rate at
which the spiral collapses towards the origin of the axes. This
method of plotting has been found particularly useful for the study
of non-linear systems, and will be considered in more detail in
Chapter 6.

The performance of more complicated servo systems

Suppose that we add some integral control to the system with

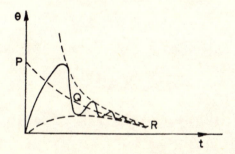

FIGURE II   *Showing the effect of adding integral control to a system
whose response curve is similar to those shown in Figure 10. The mean
misalignment falls exponentially to zero as shown by the broken line PQR.*

(Westwater and Waddell, 1961. "An Introduction to Servo Mechanisms."
English Universities Press Ltd.)

proportional control, a single exponential delay and output damping, whose performance is illustrated in *Figure 10*. The resulting
transfer function may still be solved without great difficulty by
mathematical methods, and we find that the time course of the
misalignment, when the system is considerably under-damped,
follows the line plotted in *Figure 11*. In effect, the addition of
integral control brings the steady state error towards zero, at a
rate depending on how much has been added, as is indicated by
the broken line *PQR*.

   The system may be even more elaborate than this: there may
be more than one exponential delay; there may be a finite delay
which must be treated as at least three exponential delays; there
may be inertia; and there may be error rate control as well as
integral and proportional control. It may then be impracticable,
or impossible, to discover the complete time course of the misalignment, or output, following a step function input without the use
of computers. But it is possible to discover whether the system is
unstable without actually solving the equations; and by the use
of certain "factors of safety", whether it will hunt too badly to be
acceptable.

4 RESPONSES OF SERVO SYSTEMS TO SIMPLE HARMONIC INPUTS

If the input of a servo system is given a simple harmonic motion, it means that it is increased and decreased rhythmically about its initial position: at any moment of time, moreover, the position of the input element is defined precisely by a particular kind of mathematical expression. The maximum change in either direction is the *amplitude* of the motion; the number of times that it reaches the maximum positive position (or maximum negative position) in unit time is the *frequency* of the motion. The most familiar kind of motion which is simple harmonic—or nearly so—is that of the pendulum of a clock. Other kinds of oscillatory motion, such as that of a rough sea, consist of very many simple harmonic motions superimposed on one another.

Two systems may be in simple harmonic motion at the same frequency, but they may not be in time with one another: one may reach its maximum positive position on each swing, for example, before the other one does, and there is then a difference in *phase* between them. Phase differences are of considerable importance in the study of the responses of servo systems to simple harmonic motions. They are usually expressed in terms of angles, measured in degrees or in radians. One complete cycle of the oscillation—i.e. one complete wave—from one positive position to the next, for example, occupies 360° (2π radians): in *Figure 12* (*a*) each positive peak of motion 2 occurs at the same moment as each negative peak of motion 1 (and *vice versa*), and the phase difference between them is $\frac{1}{2}$ cycle or 180° (π radians); in *Figure 12* (*b*) each positive peak of motion 2 occurs at the moment when motion 1 is passing through zero displacement on its way to a positive peak, and motion 2 has a phase *lead* of 90° ($\pi/2$ radians) with respect to motion 1; if motion 1 is on its way to a negative peak (*Figure 12* (*c*)), then motion 2 has a phase *lag* of 90° with respect to motion 1; and so on for any relation between the momentary positions of the two oscillatory systems. Since the time occupied by one complete cycle becomes smaller as the

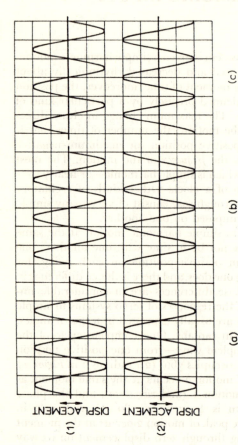

(1)
DISPLACEMENT

(2)
DISPLACEMENT

(a)

(b)

(c)

FIGURE 12 *Diagrams showing how the displacement of a system in simple harmonic motion varies with time.*

The drawings represent two such motions at the same frequency and with the same amplitude.

(a) There is a phase difference of $\frac{1}{2}$ cycle, or 180°, between motions (1) and (2): they are "out of phase".

(b) Motion (2) has a phase *lead* of $\frac{1}{4}$ cycle, or 90°, with respect to motion (1).

(c) Motion (2) has a phase *lag* of $\frac{1}{4}$ cycle, or 90°, with respect to motion (1) frequency becomes larger, the actual difference in time corresponding to a given angular phase difference also becomes smaller as the frequency becomes larger. (The reason for using these angular measures is that mathematically a simple harmonic motion is generated by a point moving round a circle; it completes one revolution, or moves through 360°, between each positive peak of the motion and the next—hence the term "cycle".)

When the input of a servo system is given a simple harmonic motion, with some particular frequency and amplitude, the output is also a simple harmonic motion with the same frequency (unless the system contains non-linear components); but in general, the output amplitude is different from the input amplitude, and there is a difference in phase between the motions. In general, also, the amplitude and phase of the output motion will vary with the frequency of the input motion (the reason for this will appear later); useful information about the performance of the servo system can be obtained only if the input is given a large number of different simple harmonic motions with different frequencies. This applies equally to the study of the relation between response and excitation of the various components which may be present in the system. For this reason, the use of simple harmonic motions for studying servo systems, often referred to as the "harmonic response method", is also known as the "frequency response method".

It is not necessary that the amplitude of the input motion should be the same at all frequencies, since at any given frequency the output amplitude is proportional to the input amplitude, and only the ratio of the one to the other, known as the "dynamic magnification", need be considered. (Again, this is not true if any of the components are non-linear, as will be discussed in Chapter 6.) The results of a study of the performance of a servo system by the frequency response method may be plotted in two ways.

(a) Two separate graphs are plotted, one of the output/input amplitude ratio (dynamic magnification) against frequency; and the other of the phase angle between output and input, also against frequency.

(b) Alternatively, amplitude and phase may be combined into a single graph which is known as a "locus". A simple harmonic motion at any given frequency can be represented graphically and

concisely by a straight line whose length defines the amplitude
of the motion. If there are two simple harmonic motions, of the
same frequency, two such lines are drawn, with different lengths
and pointing in different directions if necessary, but starting at
the same point; the angle between them indicates the difference
in phase between the two motions. These lines are known as
"vectors": not only are their lengths important, but also the
directions in which they are pointing.

Whatever the frequency of the motion, the input vector is
taken as "reference vector" and drawn with unit length and zero
phase angle (*OA* in *Figure 13*): the output vectors at the different

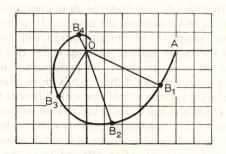

FIGURE 13   *The transfer function of a servo system, or of one of its
components, when the input is a simple harmonic motion, plotted as a locus.*
OA is the input vector, of unit length. OB_1, OB_2, OB_3 etc. are the output
vectors when the frequency is ω_1, ω_2, ω_3 etc.

frequencies are then of different lengths and point in different
directions (OB_1, OB_2, OB_3 etc,). A line drawn through their
ends (B_1, B_2, B_3 etc.) shows how the dynamic magnification and
phase difference vary with frequency. This is the "transfer locus".

As described, this locus, or the two separate graphs of dynamic
magnification and phase angle against frequency, give a picture
of the overall (closed loop) transfer function of a servo system,
when it is operating on simple harmonic motions. A corresponding
picture of the (open) loop transfer function can be obtained by
using the amplitude of the misalignment, instead of that of the
input, when calculating the dynamic magnification, and by
plotting the output–misalignment phase difference; or by using
the vector representing the motion of the misalignment element

as the "reference vector" when drawing the locus. Similar pictures can be drawn of the transfer functions of each of the components likely to be present in the servo system. The simple mathematics necessary for discovering how to draw these pictures from the known properties of the various components are given in the mathematical chapter at the end of the book. The picture of the loop transfer function of a servo system with any desired combination of components can then be constructed, and compared with that of the complete servo system that we are interested in. The transfer functions of the various components are vector quantities, and thus measures of both amplitude and phase angle. The rule for multiplying vectors is: multiply the amplitudes and add the phase angles.

Graphical representation of transfer functions. (1) Transfer loci and Nyqvist diagrams

It is useful to have a concise method of labelling the two axes of the chart on which the vectors are plotted: the axis that runs across the page is known as the "real" axis, positive towards the right and negative towards the left; the axis at right angles to it is known as the "imaginary" axis, often referred to, for shortness, as the $+j$ axis upwards and the $-j$ axis downwards. If we want to convert a vector along the positive "real" axis into one along the negative "real" axis—i.e. to rotate it through 180°—we have to multiply it by -1. If we want to convert it into one along the positive "imaginary" axis—i.e. to rotate it through 90°—we have to multiply it by something, called j, which, if the multiplication is done twice, rotates it through $2 \times 90° = 180°$; thus $j \times j = -1$, or $j = \sqrt{-1}$ and is said to be an "imaginary" number, since it cannot be evaluated. Motions, or positions, which are represented by vectors along the "imaginary" axis, however, exist just as "really" as those represented by vectors along the "real" axis.

The motor and output load. As pointed out in Chapter 3, the basic component of all servo systems is the motor, with inherent damping and an output load. Suppose, first, that the load consists only of a spring, and that there is no output velocity feedback in the motor. At any moment, the ratio of the displacement of the output element to that of the misalignment element will be determined by the relative stiffness of the motor and of the spring, sometimes referred to as the "loop gain" of the system: the stronger the motor and the weaker the spring, the greater will be the output displacement for a given misalignment. The loop transfer function of this system is identical with the loop gain, and is independent of the frequency of the applied simple harmonic motion.

On the other hand, if the load were purely frictional (with or without damping in the motor), the loop transfer function of the system would define a relation between the output *velocity* and the misalignment (Chapter 3, p. 26). This has two consequences. The velocity of an object, or system, in simple harmonic motion is measured by slope of the curve of displacement plotted against time: as may be seen in *Figure 12*, the maximum positive velocity (displacement moving towards a positive value) occurs when the displacement is zero, 90° ahead of the maximum positive displacement. The curve of velocity against time thus leads that of displacement against time by 90°. Since output velocity is proportional to misalignment, the vector representing output velocity will be along the positive "real" axis, as is that representing misalignment: since this must lead the vector representing output position by 90°, the position vector must be drawn 90° behind the velocity vector—i.e. along the negative "imaginary" axis, or $-j$ axis. Further, so long as there is, say, a positive misalignment, the motor will go on running and producing more and more positive output displacement. If the frequency of the applied simple harmonic motion is small, each half-wave lasts a long time and the motor can produce a large output displacement before it is reversed during the next half-wave: conversely, if the frequency is large, the motor is repeatedly reversed before it has had time to move the output element very far. For a given amplitude of the misalignment motion, the amplitude of the output motion is inversely proportional to the frequency, tending to infinity when the frequency approaches zero, and to zero when the frequency approaches infinity. Thus all the points defining the output amplitude for various values of the frequency, written ω (Greek omega), will lie on the $-j$ axis; and when the misalignment amplitude is made 1, their actual positions will be given by $1/\omega T_m$, where T_m is the "time constant" of the motor and its damping or frictional load (the ratio of the coefficient of friction to stiffness, or the ratio of the force/velocity relation of the motor to stiffness). These points are plotted in *Figure 14*, line (a), where T_m has been given the value 0.2. (It does not matter what units are used for time constants, so long as the same units are used for all the components of the servo system.)

Lastly, the load may be both elastic and frictional, or a purely elastic load may be moved by a motor with inherent damping. This is not uncommon in living systems: muscles, for example, may pull against elastic tissues, or against other "antagonist" muscles. On each half-wave of the motion applied to the misalignment element, the output element will tend towards the position defined by the loop gain: but since the output velocity is limited by the friction (or the output velocity feedback), it will

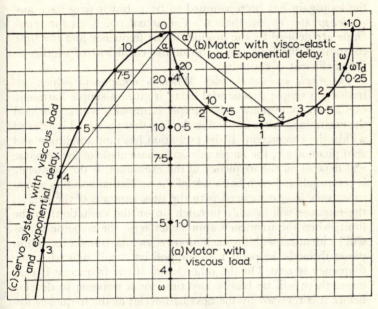

FIGURE 14 *Loop transfer loci:*

(*a*) of a very simple kind of servo system consisting of only a motor with a frictional load, or output damping (the transfer function is $-j$ $(1/\omega T_m)$ and the locus is along the $-j$ axis).

(*b*) of the same sytem with a visco-elastic load, the loop gain, G, being 1; and also of a component with an exponential delay (the transfer function is $1/(1+j\omega T_d)$ and the locus is a semi-circle).

(*c*) (on the left) of a servo system with output damping and an exponential delay, obtained by multiplying these two transfer functions together.

For the numerical values attatched to the curves, T_m ($=F/K$) has been taken as 0.2, and T_d also as 0.2. Thus the natural frequency of the system (ω_n) is 5 and the damping coefficient (ζ) is 0.5.

have time to reach this position only when the frequency is very small. As the frequency becomes larger, the system will behave more and more as if there were no elastic load, and the output displacement will lag more and more behind the misalignment, and become smaller and smaller. Mathematical analysis (given in Chapter 8) shows that the loop transfer locus is a semi-circle, below the positive real axis, as drawn in *Figure 14* line (*b*), cutting this axis, at one end, at a point defined by the loop gain, and passing through the origin at the other end. (In this drawing the loop gain has been assumed to be 1, but it may have any value, greater or less than 1.) The actual points on the semi-circle are defined by the product of the frequency and the time constant of the load (the ratio of the coefficient of friction to the coefficient of elasticity).

The simple exponential delay. When a component which introduces a simple exponential delay is given a simple harmonic excitation, its response (also simple harmonic) will lag behind the excitation; this is implied in the fact that the signal is delayed within the component. If the excitation has unit amplitude and zero phase angle, the amplitude and phase angle of the response will depend on the frequency of the excitation. If the frequency is very small and each half-cycle of the oscillation occupies a long time (very long compared with the time constant of the delay), the response will be able to catch up on the excitation: in the limit, when the frequency approaches zero, the response vector will be identical with the excitation vector; the transfer locus thus passes through the point 1 on the positive "real" axis when the frequency is zero. On the other hand, if the frequency is very large, there will be hardly any time for a response to develop before it is reversed by the next half-cycle: as the frequency approaches infinity, therefore, the amplitude of the response approaches zero, and the transfer locus passes through the origin of the axes. Mathematical analysis shows that the transfer function of a simple exponential delay has precisely the same form as the loop transfer function of the motor with a visco-elastic load when the loop gain is 1: the transfer locus is thus a semi-circle, as drawn in *Figure 14*, line (*b*). The points on the semi-circle are now defined by the product of the frequency and the time constant of the delay.

Construction of the loop transfer locus of a simple servo system. As an example, consider a servo system with a single exponential delay and a motor with frictional damping on the output element. In order to multiply together the transfer function of the delay and the loop transfer function of the motor with its load, the time constants (T_d and T_m) must be given actual values: suppose that $T_d = T_m = 0.2$. The points on the locus of the exponential delay can now be labelled with actual values of the frequency, ω. Take, for example, $\omega = 4$. The "motor vector", as measured on the graph, has a length of 1.25 and lies on the $-j$ axis: the "delay vector", measured from the origin to the point corresponding to $\omega = 4$ has a length 0.78 and is inclined at an angle of $-39°$ to the "real" axis. The product of the two is 0.99 and this, therefore, is the length of the loop transfer vector, which must be drawn at an angle of $39°$ to the left (clockwise) of the $-j$ axis. The process is repeated for other values of ω and the loop transfer locus drawn through the ends of the vectors, as shown in *Figure 14 (c)*, on the left of the diagram. Such a locus is known as a "Nyqvist diagram".

Graphical representation of transfer functions. (2) *Attenuation and phase plots (logarithmic plots)*

Plotting Nyqvist diagrams can obviously be quite laborious when there are many components whose transfer functions have to be combined. The alternative method, which has some advantages besides those of being simpler, is to take logarithms of the amplitudes of the vectors. Multiplication of their amplitudes then becomes addition of these logarithms, and this can be done directly on the chart on which the transfer functions are plotted. (When we multiply two figures on a slide rule, we add together, graphically, their logarithms.) The logarithm of the amplitude and the phase angle must now be plotted separately, and it is convenient to plot them against the logarithm of the frequency.

As the unit of log (frequency), control system engineers often use the *octave*, as is conventional among musicians: this is the logarithm of the frequency to the base 2—i.e. if the frequency is doubled or halved, it changes by ± 1 octave, respectively. The more familiar logarithm to the base 10 is also used, the unit then being the *decade*. Since $\log_2 2 = 1$ and $\log_{10} 2 = 0.301$, one octave is equal to 0.3 decades, almost exactly.

The logarithms of amplitudes are commonly called *attenuations*, and the unit developed by acoustic and tele-communication engineers has been adopted: this is the *decibel*. If a signal with unit amplitude is given to some component, and the output, or response, is A times greater—i.e. if the length of the output vector in the transfer locus is A—then the attenuation is $20 \log_{10} A$ decibels. A may be greater or less than 1, and thus the attenuation may be positive or negative.

The motor with viscous load or output damping. (Figure 15.) The

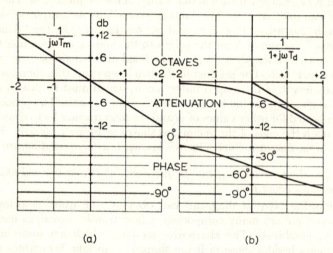

(a)   (b)

FIGURE 15 *Attenuation and phase diagrams of the same transfer functions as drawn as loci (Nyqvist diagrams) in Figure 14.*

(a) the motor and associated damping;
(b) a simple exponential delay.

graph relating attenuation to log (frequency) is a straight line, with a slope of -6 dB per octave, or -20 dB per decade: it passes through o (i.e. the dynamic magnification is 1) when the frequency is equal to the reciprocal of the time constant—i.e. when $\omega = 1/T_m$. The phase angle, as already pointed out, is $-90°$ at all frequencies.

Simple exponential delay. (Figure 15.) Very approximately, the relation between attenuation and log (frequency) may be represented by two straight lines or "asymptotes", one along the axis of log (frequency) at o attenuation, when the frequency is small, and the other sloping downwards at -6 dB per octave when the frequency is large. The two lines meet when the frequency (ω) is equal to the reciprocal of the time constant of the delay—i.e. when $\omega = 1/T_d$; this is known as the "corner frequency". Actually, at this frequency the attenuation is -3 dB, not o dB, but nowhere does the "divergence" of the true curve from the two symptotes exceed this amount. For many purposes, indeed, the whole curve can be drawn, with sufficient accuracy without further information; but extra help is provided by the fact that at 1 octave above and below the corner frequency the divergence from the asymptote is almost exactly -1 dB.

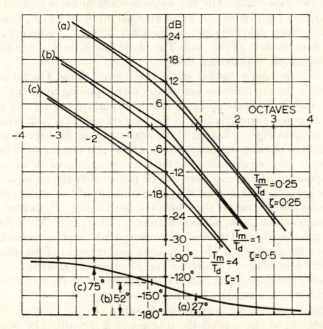

FIGURE 16 *Attenuation and phase diagrams of the servo system with a simple exponential delay, as drawn in Figure 14 as a Nyqvist diagram.*

Three attenuation curves are shown with: (a) $T_m/T_d=0.25$; $\zeta=0.25$; (b) $T_m/T_d=1$, $\zeta=0.5$; and (c) $T_m/T_d=4$, $\zeta=1.0$. The phase margins inserted on the phase curve.

The curve of phase angle against log (frequency) is asymptotic to o° and $-90°$ when ω approaches o and ∞ respectively. The phase angle is $-45°$ at the corner frequency: at one octave above

C

and below the corner frequency, it is $-45° \pm 18.5°$; at 2 octaves from the corner frequency it is $-45° \pm 21°$; and so on, for greater and smaller frequencies.

(All the figures given in the previous paragraphs are derived from simple mathematical expressions which will be found in Chapter 8.)

The motor with visco-elastic load. The attenuation line has the same form as that of a simple exponential delay, but shifted along the attenuation axis. The low frequency asymptote is parallel to the axis of log (frequency) at an attenuation of $20 \log_{10}G$, where G is the loop gain: the corner frequency is at $1/T_0$, where T_0 is the time constant of the load. The phase line is the same as that of the simple exponential delay.

The loop transfer function of the simple servo system. On adding together the attenuations and phases corresponding to the motor with its associated damping and to the exponential delay, we get the diagrams corresponding to the loop transfer functions which are given in *Figure 16*. One of the advantages of the logarithmic method of plotting frequency response curves is that we need use, initially, only the asymptotes of the attenuation lines of the various components: the divergences can be put in after the asymptotes have been added together. The time constant of one of the components (usually that of the motor and its damping, T_m) is used to define 0 octave on the scale of frequency; the attenuation is then 0 at this frequency. The corner frequency of the exponential delay is then at $\log_2(T_m/T_d)$ where T_d is the time constant of the delay. For the central line, T_d has been taken equal to T_m and the corner frequency of the delay is thus at 0 octave. Below (to the left of) the corner, the attenuation line has a slope of $(-6 + 0) = -6$ dB/octave: above the corner, the slope is $(-6 + (-6)) = -12$ dB/octave; at the corner, the divergence is -3 dB. The phase curves are the same as those of the exponential delay alone, but shifted by $-90°$ (i.e. downwards). These lines define the same loop transfer function as has been plotted as a locus in *Figure 14*. For the other two lines, T_d has been made $\frac{1}{4}T_m$ and $4T_m$ respectively: the corner frequency is shifted to $+2$ octaves and -2 octaves and the attenuation and phase lines are shifted up and down, and to the right and left, accordingly.

It is obviously much easier to draw these lines than to plot a transfer locus. Suppose a third component had to be added, another exponential delay for example. If this had the same time constant as the first, the slope of the attenuation line below the corner would be unchanged, the slope above the corner would be $(-6 + (-6) + (-6)) = -18$ dB/octave, and the divergence at the corner would be -6 dB: the phase at any frequency would be $-90°$ *plus* twice the value for a single delay at that frequency. If the third component (or any further additional one) had a different time constant, its corner frequency, in octaves, would be calculated from its time constant (with respect to that of the motor) in the same way as was that of the exponential delay. Some kinds of component, of course, may have positive phase angles and attenuation lines with positive slopes: the rules for adding together the phase angles, the slopes of the attenuation lines and the divergencies (all with due regard to sign) still hold. An example will be given in a later section.

Graphical representation of overall transfer functions

The overall transfer locus of a servo system can be plotted from the loop transfer locus (Nyqvist diagram) by means of a simple graphical construction which is described in Chapter 8 (p. 171). There is no simple way by which overall transfer functions can be derived graphically from loop transfer functions when these are in the logarithmic form. Usually, however, not much is gained by plotting overall transfer functions when the frequency response method is used: as will appear later, all the necessary information about the behaviour of the servo system can be obtained from the loop transfer function.

The frequency response of a system capable of oscillating. Resonance

As discussed in the previous chapter, servo systems in which there is inertia on the output element, a simple exponential delay, or integral control, as well as proportional control and viscous friction on the output element, are capable of oscillating. Whether they will do so, and whether the oscillations die away more or less gradually, maintain a constant amplitude, or build up progressively, depends on the value of the "damping coefficient". When any system, or component, is given an oscillating (simple harmonic) input or stimulus over a suitable range of frequencies, the possibility that it will hunt after being given a step function input, and how badly it will do so, is indicated by the existence of "resonance". If the input amplitude is kept constant, independent of frequency, the output amplitude rises to a maximum value (the "resonance peak") when the input frequency is close to the natural frequency of the oscillating system. By means of mathematical analysis, it is found that:

(1) when the input frequency equals the natural frequency of the system, the output lags behind the input by $\frac{1}{4}$ cycle (the phase angle is $-90°$) whatever the value of the damping coefficient; (2) at this frequency, the dynamic magnification (output/input amplitude ratio) is inversely proportional to the damping coefficient (ζ), being 0.5 when $\zeta = 1.0$ (the damping is critical), 1.0 when $\zeta = 0.5$ and infinite when $\zeta = 0$ (the natural oscillations are maintained indefinitely); (3) a "resonance peak" appears in

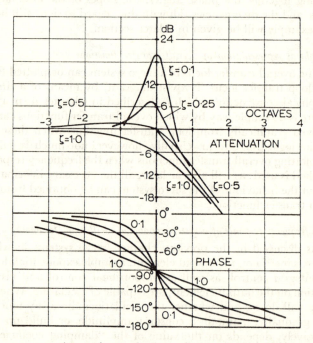

FIGURE 17   *Attenuation and phase diagrams of a component, or system, which is capable of oscillation.*

These show the frequency response curves, with different values of the damping coefficient, of a component with a complex exponential delay: they are also the overall frequency response curves of servo systems with, say, a simple exponential delay, corresponding to the overall transfer loci drawn in *Figure 38* (p. 172).

the dynamic magnification when $\zeta = 0.7$ or less, the "resonant frequency" at which this peak appears being equal to the natural frequency when $\zeta = 0$, and slightly less than this (depending on the value of ζ) when ζ is greater than 0; the magnitude of the resonance peak rises as ζ falls from 0.7 towards 0.

These points are illustrated in the attenuation and phase diagrams given in *Figure 17*. These have been plotted from the mathematical expression which defines the overall (closed loop) transfer function of a servo system capable of oscillation when it is given a simple harmonic input. Whatever the value of ζ the two asymptotes are: when the frequency approaches zero, a line along the attenuation axis (i.e. attenuation = 0); when the frequency approaches infinity, a line sloping downwards at -12 dB/octave; the corner is at the natural frequency of the system. The divergence of the true curve from the asymptotes at the corner frequency depends on the value of ζ: when $\zeta = 1$ it is -6 dB; when $\zeta = 0.5$ it is 0 dB; when $\zeta = 0$, it is $+\infty$. The phase angles of the oscillating system are similar in shape to those of the exponential delay. They are negative for all values of the frequency, approaching 0 and $-180°$ as the frequency approaches 0 and ∞ respectively. At the corner frequency, when the phase angle is $-90°$, the curves become progressively steeper as ζ becomes smaller. The attenuation and phase lines of a critically damped system are identical with those of two exponential delays, with the same time constant, in series.

As shown in *Figure 17*, when the damping is about one-half the critical value, the attenuation remains nearly constant as the frequency is increased to the natural frequency of the system, and the resonance peak is barely noticeable. This is another way of showing that if small amounts of overshoot are acceptable, the system responds more rapidly if the damping is rather less than critical (compare the response to step function inputs given in *Figure 10*, p. 41).

The relatively simple systems considered in detail in this and the previous chapters will hunt, or become unstable, only when the loop is closed. But this is not necessarily so: if the system contains a component which introduces a complex delay, for example, this component might oscillate on its own even when the loop is open; or there might be subsidiary closed loops within the "controller" box of the block diagram in *Figure 1*, producing local oscillations. (In an electrical system, one of the amplifiers might be oscillating—"howling" or "ringing".) When constructing a servo system, using known components, which will imitate some particular system that is under test, it may sometimes be necessary to include one which has the general properties of a complex exponential delay or other local oscillating component. The transfer function of such a component will be represented by one of the curves in the attenuation and phase diagrams given in *Figure 17*.

Detection of instability in an oscillating system

When a system is capable of continuous oscillation ($\zeta = 0$ or is negative), the overall transfer function goes to infinity when the frequency of the applied simple harmonic motion is made equal to the natural frequency of the system: the properties of such a system must obviously be studied with the loop open. The loop transfer function does, however, provide definite information as to whether a system is actually unstable, and some information as to how badly it will hunt even though it is strictly stable.

In nearly all servo systems, the phase lag of the output with respect to the misalignment becomes progressively more negative as the frequency of the motion increases. Suppose that at some particular frequency, it becomes exactly $-180°$ ($\frac{1}{2}$ cycle) so that the signal is exactly reversed as it passes from the misalignment detector to the output element. If the loop were closed in these conditions, at the moment when the misalignment detector receives a signal from the input element with, say, a maximum positive amplitude, it receives one from the output element with a maximum negative amplitude. Subtraction of this negative signal from the positive one at the misalignment detector is equivalent to addition of a positive signal: the misalignment signal is now the sum of the input and output signals, instead of the difference between them. So long as the output amplitude is less than the misalignment amplitude (the dynamic magnification is less than 1, or the attenuation is negative), this is of no great consequence. But suppose that the dynamic magnification is equal to 1 (the attenuation is zero). We now have: (output) $= -$(misalignment). But when the loop is closed, we also have: (misalignment) $=$ (input) $-$ (output). Thus the system can have an output and a misalignment in the absence of any input; any small disturbance which may arise accidentally within the system, with a component at the critical frequency, will produce continuous oscillation. If the dynamic magnification is greater than 1 (the attenuation is positive), the amplitude of the signal will become progressively greater each time it passes round the closed loop. The oscillations will grow rapidly, with perhaps catastrophic effects on the whole system.

When studying the system with the loop open, therefore, and plotting the results as logarithmic attenuation and phase lines, it will be stable, in the sense of not going into permanent oscillation when the loop is closed, if either: (a) the attenuation is negative when the phase angle is $-180°$; or (b) the phase angle is positive to $-180°$ when the attenuation is zero.

When the results are plotted in the form of a combined amplitude and phase locus, the output becomes equal to the misalignment with the sign reversed—i.e. the dynamic magnification is 1 and the phase angle is $-180°$—when the point representing the output is at -1 on the negative "real" axis. If the loop transfer locus passes through this point, the system will just be unstable when the loop is closed. The criterion for stability, therefore, is that if we were to travel along the loop transfer locus in the direction of increasing frequency, we must leave the point $(-1, j.0)$ on our left: if we leave it on our right (pass outside it), the system is unstable. This is the *Nyqvist criterion* of stability. (There are some exceptions to this simple rule, but they are rare.)

Gain and phase margins. Even though a system may be strictly stable according to these criteria, this does not mean that it will necessarily settle down sufficiently rapidly after a sudden change in input to be acceptable in practice. There must be an adequate "margin" both of attenuation (or gain) and of phase. Empirically it has been found that the "gain margin", or the distance between the point $(-1, j.0)$ and the point where the loop transfer locus crosses the negative "real" axis, must be at least 0.5; or in other words, at the frequency at which the phase angle is $-180°$, the dynamic magnification must be less than 0.5, or the attenuation must be negative and at least -6 dB. There must also be an adequate "phase margin": at the frequency at which the dynamic magnification is 1 (the attenuation is zero) the phase angle must be positive to $-180°$ by at least $40°$.

Systems which have only a single simple exponential delay do not become unstable, unless there is no damping at all. The phase of the output never reaches $-180°$, so that the gain margin is always adequate. As shown in *Figure 17*, however, the phase margin falls as the damping coefficient becomes smaller (as is, indeed, to be expected). The system with $T_d = T_m$ and $\zeta = 0.5$ (curve (b)) has a phase margin of 52°, an adequate value; and as may be seen in *Figure 10* (p. 41) such a system does not hunt excessively. When $T_d = 4T_m$ and $\zeta = 0.25$, the phase margin is 27°, less than the desirable value, and the system would hunt excessively.

The frequency response of a system with a finite delay

The effect on the performance of a system of adding a component which introduces a finite delay can be discovered quite easily when the frequency response is studied. The component introduces a constant time delay, independent of the frequency of the motion applied to it, but has no effect on the amplitude of the motion. As the frequency becomes greater, the response thus

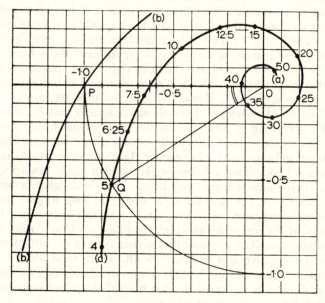

FIGURE 18   *Nyqvist diagrams of a system with a finite delay*

The delay time is 0.2 for both curves. The time constant of the motor (damping/stiffness ratio) is 0.2 (curve (a)) and 0.127 (curve (b): the reduction of the frictional damping, or the increase in stiffness is just sufficient to produce an unstable system.

lags in phase behind the excitation by an angle which increases in proportion to the frequency: when the time delay is just equal to half the time taken for the excitation to complete one cycle, the phase lag becomes −180°, which is the same as a phase lead of +180°. On increasing the frequency still further, the phase lead becomes smaller, and reaches zero when the natural period of the motion is equal to the time delay: thereafter, there is again a phase lag, and so on. The *transfer locus* is, in fact, a circle of unit radius with the origin as centre.

In the *logarithmic plots*, the attenuation is zero at all frequencies; the angle of phase lag, proportional to the frequency is represented by a curve (the scale of frequency is logarithmic), asymptotic to 0° as the frequency approaches 0 and becoming progressively steeper as the frequency increases (*Figure 19*).

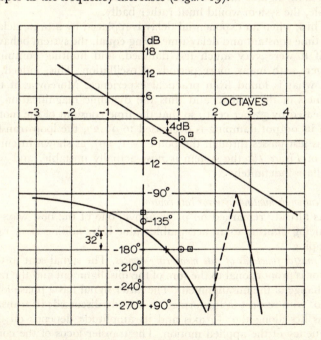

FIGURE 19 *Attenuation and phase diagrams of a system with a finite delay and output damping (by viscous friction or negative velocity feedback)*

The gain margin is 4 dB and the phase margin is 32°. The circles and squares show the effect of adding phase advance (see text).

C*

The loop transfer function of a servo system in which the time constant of the motor and its damping is 0.2 as before, and there is a finite delay with a delay time of 0.2, is plotted as a locus in *Figure 18* and as attenuation and phase lines in *Figure 19*, the methods of construction being the same as those already described. The lengths of the vectors, and the attenuations, are the same as those for the motor alone: the phase of each vector is asymptotic to —90°, the constant phase angle of the motor, as the frequency approaches 0. The phase lag increases progressively as the frequency increases, and becomes —180° when the frequency is 7.85 (at +0.65 octave). The system has a gain margin of 0.36 from the transfer locus (*Figure 18*) or 4 dB from the attenuation line (*Figure 19*); and a phase margin of 32° (the angle *POQ* in *Figure 18*). Both figures are too small to be acceptable: while strictly stable, the system would hunt rather badly.

Thus, when an exponential delay is replaced by a finite delay, the time constant and delay time being equal, the system behaves as if it were very much less damped, and hunting continues longer, with many more periods of oscillation. This, indeed, is just what is found from practical experience. Moreover, if the stiffness of the system, and thus the dynamic magnification, is increased by 57 per cent., so that the time constant of the motor and its output damping is decreased to 0.127, the loop transfer locus just passes through the point $(-1, j.0)$, as shown in curve (b) of *Figure 18*: the system is now actually unstable, and will oscillate indefinitely.

Prevention of hunting by error rate control

As already remarked on p. 37 above, one of the best ways of reducing hunting to an acceptable value is by adding error rate damping.

Transfer functions of rate measuring devices. The signal sent to the motor is proportional to the sum of the misalignment and the rate of change of the misalignment. The latter signal has a phase lead of 90° with respect to the former, as already discussed: its transfer locus lies along the $+j$ axis and its amplitude depends on the frequency of the applied motion. The transfer locus of the combined signals, as demonstrated in the mathematical section in Chapter 8, p. 168, is a semi-circle of the same size as that representing the transfer locus of an exponential delay, but on the $+j$ side of the positive "real" axis, instead of on the $-j$ side.

Stabilisation by error rate control is often referred to as "phase advance stabilisation".

The attenuation and phase lines, also, will be the same as those of an exponential delay with the signs reversed—i.e. turned upside down about the axis of log (frequency). Addition of a phase advancing component has the further effect of making the total gain at high frequencies greater than it was before. This is another way of expressing the fact that the system is given an

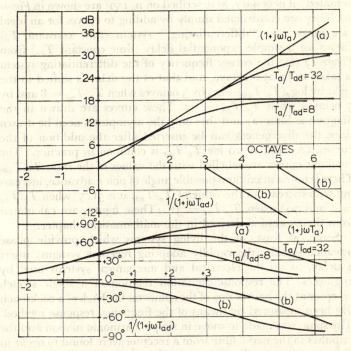

FIGURE 20 *Attenuation and phase diagrams of phase advancing (differentiating) systems (with "gain compensation").*

The attenuation and phase curves of an "ideal" system are shown in curves (a), the transfer function being $(1+j\omega T_a)$. A "practical" system has in addition an exponential delay, the transfer function being $1/1=j\omega T_{ad}$: the attenuation and phase curves are shown in curves (b). The remaining curves, labelled $T_a/T_{ad}=32$ and $T_a/T_{ad}=8$, show the combined values of attenuation and phase when the ratio of the time constants has these values.

additional boost when the input is changing rapidly (compare p. 38); but it complicates the process of finding the best parameters of the phase advance system for removing instability or reducing hunting.

In practice, as pointed out in Chapter 3, p. 34, all devices for introducing error rate control also introduce a delay, which must be included when a complete servo system is being constructed from the transfer functions of its components. The attenuation and phase lines for a practical phase advance system ("gain compensated" if necessary, as described on p. 159) are shown in *Figure 20*. They are constructed simply by adding to curves for an ideal rate measuring ("differentiating") system (time constant T_a) curves for a simple exponential delay (time constant T_{ad}) from *Figure 14 (b)*: the corner frequency of the differentiating system is taken to be at 0 octave, and that of the delay is shifted to the right by $\log_2(T_a/T_{ad})$—i.e. by 3 octaves when $T_a/T_{ad} = 8$ and by 5 octaves when $T_a/T_{ad} = 32$. These curves are drawn in the diagram as lines (a) and (b): only the asymptotes need be drawn since the divergences can be inserted after the addition of the curves. (A value of 20 for T_a/T_{ad} is common in practice.) The resultant curves are labelled with the values of the ratio T_a/T_{ad}. There is now a maximum possible angle of phase advance, increasing with increase in the value of T_a/T_{ad}; it is 51.5° when $T_a/T_{ad} = 8$ and 70° when $T_a/T_{ad} = 32$. (These figures are calculated from the expression derived in the mathematical chapter.)

Some, at least, of the living systems which provide phase advance signals (the rapidly adapting receptor systems) insert a delay, as do the electrical and mechanical systems used by engineers. The response/excitation relation of a single stretch receptor at the base of one of the spines on the back of a cockroach has been measured by means of the frequency response method. The spine was made to move in simple harmonic motion and the impulses in the nerve fibre from a receptor were found to occur in groups, one group for each cycle of displacement. In each group the maximum response (as defined by the minimum interval between successive impulses) occurred before the amplitude of the displacement reached a maximum—i.e. the response was advanced in phase with respect to the excitation. The maximum phase advance occurred at a frequency of 0.5 cycle per second, and was 52°: one may thus infer that the differentiating system possessed a delay component with a time constant one-eighth of that of the differentiating component. Mathematical analysis of the rate at which the impulse frequency declined after a sudden (step function) displacement suggested, however, that the delay was not a simple exponential one, but was much more complicated. It was necessary to assume, of course, that the response/excitation relation was linear, and it is possible that the apparent complexity of the delay was actually a reflection of the non-linearity of the response. Some other kinds of rapidly adapting receptor seem to produce a greater phase advance than would be expected from simple theoretical considerations: this may also be due to non-linearity and will be discussed in Chapter 7.

Loop transfer functions of systems with error rate control. Since the transfer function of an "ideal" rate measuring device is the inverse of that of a simple exponential delay, it is obvious that if such devices were available, the effects of the delay could be completely removed by choosing one which had the same time constant as that of the delay. Even with "practical" devices, the performance of systems with simple exponential delays can be made satisfactory without difficulty. If there were no output damping at all, the delay associated with the differentiating device would have to have a time constant not less than 5 times that of the differentiating device itself, in order to provide a phase margin somewhat greater than the minimum of 40°—but this can be achieved without difficulty.

When there is a finite delay, however, the matter is not so simple. Suppose that we decide to improve the performance of the system with a finite delay, whose attenuation and phase lines are given in *Figure 19*, by adding a phase advancing component. The phase margin must be increased by 8° to bring it up to the required 40°: from *Figure 20* we see that such a phase advance would be provided by either of the plotted curves at about 2.5 octaves below the corner frequency. We could thus use a differentiating system with a corner at about $+2.5$ octaves with respect to the frequency (ω) at which the attenuation is 0. This is where $\omega = 1/T_m$, where T_m is the time constant of the motor and its output damping; since in this system the delay time (T_f) is equal to T_m, we have $T_a/T_f = 1/5.6$. But in order to allow for the increase in gain, we increase the phase advance slightly and take $T_a/T_f = 1/4$, the corner frequency being at $+2$ octaves. The phase margin is now increased by 14.5° and becomes 46.5°: the phase line reaches $-180°$ a little beyond $+1$ octave, there is an increased gain of just over 1 dB (see the attenuation curve for the phase advance system at -1 octave), and the gain margin is increased to 5.5 dB. (The relevant points are marked by circles in *Figure 19*). If we increase the amount of phase advance by increasing T_a/T_f to 1/2, the phase margin is increased still further (to nearly 60°), the phase reaches $-180°$ at 1.3 octaves, there is an increased gain of 4 dB and the gain margin returns once more to the intial value of 4 dB. (The relevant points are marked by squares in *Figure 19*.) The value of 1/4 for T_a/T_f is about the best that can be chosen, but even so the performance of the system would be barely satisfactory.

The matter, however, is even worse than this would suggest. If we tried to give the system an even greater phase margin, made $T_a/T_f = 1$ and used a differentiating device with a large value of T_a/T_{ad}, the attenutation of the complete system would be positive from 0 octave to about 1.5 octaves, and zero for some 2 octaves further. (This may be seen by comparing the attenuation curves in *Figures 15* and *19*; the slope of the phase advance curve is $+6$ dB/octave, and that of the motor and its damping is -6 dB/octave.) The phase angle will now reach $-180°$ at a frequency at which the attenuation is zero: we are worse off than we were to begin with, and the system has been made actually unstable.

We may conclude that severe hunting in systems with finite delays cannot be suppressed without increasing the frictional (or output velocity) damping and so also increasing the steady state velocity error. This error may be reduced again by the addition of input feed forward, as appears to be done in some living control systems, where finite delays are common. On the other hand, as we shall see in the next chapter, the receptors which measure displacements and velocities in living systems have non-linear properties; it is possible that large phase advances may be provided without so much increase in gain as is necessary in linear systems.

Analysis of a living control system by the frequency response method. The pupil reflex controlling the amount of light entering the eye

Most people are aware that the sensitivity of their eyes varies according to the intensity of the surrounding illumination; but few, probably, realise how large these changes are. If someone goes from bright sunlight into a completely dark room and stays there for some time, the sensitivity of his eyes gradually increases, eventually by a factor of some 10 millions. The greater part of this change is brought about by a change in the sensitivity of the receptor cells in the retina of the eye, just as a photographer may select a film or plate with an emulsion of the appropriate sensitivity or "speed". Such changes in sensitivity occur slowly, and may take up to an hour or more. There is also a more rapid method by which the eyes are "adapted" to changing illumination and that is by adjusting the size of the pupil and altering the fraction of the light which penetrates through to the retina. A contraction, or "narrowing" of the pupil can easily be seen by looking at the eyes of someone who has been in a dimly lit room and then suddenly shining a bright light on them. A photographer, similarly, reduces the aperture of his lens—"stops it down" and uses a larger F-number—when in bright surroundings.

Changes in the size of the pupil are brought about quite unconsciously by a control system in which the input is the intensity of the light falling on the outside of the eye (strictly the "light flux"): the motor is the system of muscle fibres in the iris, one set circular, constricting the pupil when they contract, and the other set radial, dilating it when they contract; the misalignment is the light flux actually falling on the retina and setting up nerve impulses in the optic nerve; and the controller consists of a rather elaborate set of nerve cells and synapses in the nervous system. In order to determine the loop transfer function of the system it is necessary to open the loop so that the action of the motor has no effect on the misalignment. In the particular series of experiments to be discussed this was done by arranging that the only light reaching the retina entered the eye in a narrow "pencil" whose diameter was less than that of the pupil in the conditions used, as indicated by *Figure 21* (*a*). The intensity of this pencil of light was modulated in simple harmonic motion at any desired frequency, the amplitude of the modulations being a small fraction of the intensity (so as to reduce as far as possible the effects of non-linearities). The diameter of the pupil was measured by observing it in infra-red light (by means of suitable photo-electric cells) to which the eye is completely insensitive.

The loop transfer function. The results of the measurements are plotted as attenuation and phase curves in *Figure 22*. The attenuation curve has a low frequency asymptote with zero slope, and a high frequency asymptote with a slope of -18 dB/octave: this would be consistent with the existence of three exponential delays in the system with nearly the same time constants (compare

Figure 15 (b)). Extrapolation of the asymptotes indicates that the corner frequency was 1.7 c/s (plotted as 0 octave), so that the time constant of the delays was about 0.1 second.

The results may be interpreted in two ways, which are not mutually exclusive. The muscles which act as motors may be

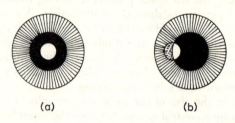

(a)   (b)

FIGURE 21   *Arrangement for studying the frequency response of the control system which regulates the size of the pupil in man.*

The subject's eye is viewed from the front: the radial lines represent the iris; the black circle shows the part of the lens not covered by the iris and its area is the area of the pupil; the white circle is a cross section of the pencil of light shining into the eye.

In (a) the variations in the size of the pupil are too small to obscure any part of the pencil of light and do not affect the illumination of the retina: the servo loop is open.

In (b) small variations in the size of the pupil have a large effect on the amount of light reaching the retina: the loop is closed, the gain large and the system is unstable. (From Stark and Sherman, *Journal of Neurophysiology* vol. 20, pp. 17–26, (1957.)

opposed by a visco-elastic load, having to stretch the antagonist muscles which themselves are in a state of partial activity: the time constant of this load must be approximately the same as that of the exponential delays. Alternatively, the muscles, with their inherent output velocity feedback, may be opposed by a negligible load, or one which is purely frictional. If this were so, the low frequency asymptote should have a slope of −6 dB/octave (compare *Figure 15 (a)* and *Figure 16*): that it has zero slope might be due to the presence of a phase advancing component, which would have a slope of +6 dB/octave (*Figure 20*). That there is such a component is confirmed by direct experimental observation. If the illumination falling on the eye is suddenly increased, the pupil constricts: but if the illumination is then kept constant, the pupil dilates again; the control system responds to the rate of change of illumination as well as to the absolute intensity of the illumination. In order to account for the attenuation being −17 dB at low frequencies, we can suppose that the corner frequency of the phase advance component is at 2.85 octaves with respect to the frequency at which the attenuation introduced by the motor is zero (2.85 octaves at −6 dB/octave = −17 dB); this implies that the

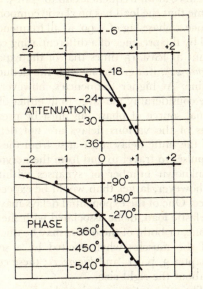

FIGURE 22 *Attenuation and phase diagrams for the pupil control system in man.*

The frequency is in octaves about the observed corner frequency (1.7 c/s). The attenuation is in decibels, calculated as described in the text, and the phase angle is in degrees.

(Plotted from data in *Stark and Sherman, Journal of Neurophysiology*, vol. 20, pp. 17–26 (1957).

time constant of the motor (T_m) is 7.1 times that of the differentiating component (T_a) $(\log_2 7.1 = 2.85)$. The time constant of the exponential delays must be substantially smaller than T_a, but we cannot say more than this in the absence of measurements at sufficiently low frequencies.

When analysing the phase line, we have to allow for the

existence of a finite delay. From the response to a sudden change in the intensity of illumination (step function input) the magnitude of the delay was estimated to be 0.18 second. We now add together the phase angles introduced by: (1) the exponential delays (3 times the phase angles read off from *Figure 16 (b)*); and (2) the finite delay (calculated as 0.18 $f \times 360°$, where f is the frequency in c/s). The curve so found agrees approximately with the observed curve at all frequencies up to +0.5. octave If, however, we assume that the load has no elastic component, the motor would introduce a phase lag of $-90°$ at all frequencies: this would be eliminated by the presence of a differentiating component with a time constant at least 15 times that of the exponential delays (compare *Figure 22*), in agreement with the deductions from the attenuation line. At higher frequencies, however, the observed phase lags are considerably too large to fit either of these systems; some additional source of phase lag must be present.

The origins of the various delays are not definitely known. Some part of the finite delay must arise from the time taken for the nerve impulses to travel to and from the nervous system, and across the unknown number of synapses within the nervous system; it is, however, larger than would be expected if this were the only source. One of the exponential delays may be introduced by the visco-elastic load, or be associated with the differentiating component: one, or both, of the others may be due to the gradual shortening of the muscles when excited by a series of stimuli (compare Chapter 3, p. 31, and *Figure 7*); these could have time constants of about the right size.

Instability. The attenuations, as plotted in *Figure 22*, are deduced from the output/misalignment amplitude ratios, calculated in the following way. The misalignment amplitude is equal to the input amplitude, since the loop has been opened, and this is the amplitude of the intensity modulation applied to the pencil of light entering the eye. The output amplitude is calculated from the amplitude of the fluctuations in pupil area, as measured; but in order to make the ratio dimensionless, it is expressed as the amplitude of the fluctuations in light intensity on the retina which would occur if the diameter of the pencil of light were larger than that of the pupil—i.e. if the loop were closed. The attenuations are all negative, so that the system is stable even when the phase angle becomes $-180°$. But if the narrow pencil of light used to illuminate the eye is made eccentric, as shown in *Figure 21* (b), much of it is obscured by the iris, and a small change in the diameter of the pupil now makes a large change in the amount of light reaching the retina. The loop is closed, the gain of the system is larger than it would be in normal conditions, and the attenuation may become zero, or even positive. The system was observed to become unstable, and the diameter of the pupil to oscillate, in the absence of any modulation of the beam of light: the frequency of the oscillation was very nearly the same as that at which the phase angle became $-180°$ in the open loop condition. In this respect, therefore, the system behaved in just the way that would be expected from control system theory.

5 NON-LINEARITY IN LIVING SYSTEMS

The properties of the components of living systems, described qualitatively in Chapter 2, must now be studied quantitatively, in order to discover whether their transfer functions are linear; and if not, what particular kinds of non-linearity are present, so that appropriate methods may be used for analysing the control systems concerned.

We are immediately faced with a problem of some difficulty. A series of inputs, or excitatory stimuli, of different known magnitudes, must be applied to the component studied, and the magnitude of the output, or response, to each stimulus measured: a plot of response *versus* excitation will show what kind of non-linearity is present. There is no difficulty, in principle at least, in measuring the magnitude of the stimulus to a receptor cell, or association oi receptor cells in a "sense organ"; whether it be a change of length or other kind of mechanical deformation, a change in temperature, a change in illumination, or the rate at which any of these changes is applied. Again, there is no difficulty in measuring the response of an effector cell, or association of effector cells—the force exerted by a muscle or the amount of some substance secreted or transported in unit time. But the response of the receptors and the stimulus to the effectors consist of trains of nerve impulses, and this is where the difficulty comes in.

In any single nerve fibre the magnitude of the signal that it is transmitting may be measured in terms of the time interval between successive impulses; or if this is constant, in terms of the frequency of the impulses. But as components of some particular control system, we are concerned with all the receptor cells, all the effector cells and all the nerve fibres and nerve cells connecting them, which may be brought into action. The receptor cells do not all have the same response/excitation relation, nor do the nerve cells or effector cells (this is known from experimental evidence): we require to know, therefore, the frequency of the impulses in each of the nerve fibres, remembering that at any particular moment some of them may be transmitting no impulses at all. The number of nerve fibres may be no more than about 10, but in vertebrates particularly, it is much more likely to be several hundred, or perhaps several thousand. It is impracticable to measure the impulse frequency in each fibre separately—even if this were technically feasible—but fortunately it is possible to make some estimate of the total impulse frequency in all the fibres by putting recording electrodes on the nerve "trunk" in which they are included.

In such a nerve trunk each fibre is surrounded by "tissue fluid" which is a conductor of electricity and which "shunts", or partly short-circuits, the electric changes associated with the nerve impulses. Even though each nerve impulse is an "all-or-nothing" event, the electric changes recorded from a whole bundle of nerve fibres are not. Each nerve fibre acts like a battery, which has a large internal resistance, connected to a load with a much smaller resistance: by putting more batteries in parallel, we decrease the internal resistance, send more current through the load, and increase the voltage drop across it. The size of the electric change which reaches the recording electrodes at any moment is only a small part of the electric change accompanying a nerve impulse in any one of the fibres, and depends on the fraction of the fibres which are carrying impulses at that moment. The time integral of the recorded electric changes is thus an approximate measure of the integrated impulse frequency in all the fibres in the nerve trunk. It must be admitted, however, that this is not necessarily a useful quantity to measure: we are by no means certain, for example, that one fibre carrying, say, 100 impulses per second conveys the same message as 10 fibres each carrying 10 impulses per second; indeed, in some circumstances it is unlikly that this would be true.

We are left, therefore, with the necessity of making such inferences as we can about the properties of populations of receptor cells, nerve cells and effector cells from the properties of single cells. These, in suitable circumstances, can be measured, and show that there must be limits beyond which populations of any of these kinds of cell cannot give responses which are linearly related to the excitations, and suggest what kind of non-linearity may be present between these limits.

In a few circumstances these difficulties do not arise. Some muscles and secreting glands respond to the presence of specific hormones in the blood which reaches them: the relation between the magnitude of the response and the rate of supply of hormone could be measured without insuperable difficulty, but this does not seem to have been attempted systematically.

Receptors

The earliest attempts to measure the response/excitation relations of receptors were based on sensations experienced by human subjects. The actual magnitude of a sensation cannot be measured directly; the subject can do little more than say whether a sensation is present or not, and whether one sensation is greater or less than another. It is possible to find the smallest changes in the magnitude of the stimulus (measured in the appropriate physical or chemical units) which can just be appreciated, and this is known as the *differential threshold*. If a subject's hand rests, palm upwards, on a table, and each of a pair of different weights is placed successively on one of his fingers, he can say whether one is heavier than the other. Alternatively, and rather more precisely, he can detect differences between the weights by estimating the amount of muscular "effort" needed to lift his hand, supporting the weight, from the table. The results of a large number of such experimental observations were reported by the German physiologist E. H. Weber in 1846. Over a wide range of weights (e.g. 200 grams to 2000 grams) the differential threshold (which we may write as $\triangle S$) was a constant fraction of the actual weight, S— i.e. the ratio $\triangle S/S$ was constant. If the weights were very small or very large, the ratio increased and the "sensitivity" became smaller. It is an obvious mathematical consequence of the constancy of the ratio $\triangle S/S$ (which became known as "Weber's law") that the magnitude of the sensation, or response to the stimulus, if this could be measured, would be proportional to the *logarithm* of the stimulus. This was pointed out by Fechner in 1860 in the course of a very extended series of such measurements.

One must be extremely cautious in using evidence from subjective sensations as evidence of the properties of the receptor cells, or even of those of the populations of receptor cells which act as misalignment detectors in living control systems. The nerve impulses from the receptor cells pass through a great many nerve cells on their way through the nervous system; there is a great deal of interaction, not only between impulses from different cells in the same population, but also, possibly, with impulses from receptor cells of quite different kinds. The sensation produced by a given stimulus may depend on the amount of stimulation given previously, and on the presence or absence, simultaneously or previously, of stimuli of quite different kinds. There is, nevertheless, some general correspondence between the magnitudes of some rather simple kinds of sensation and the responses of the receptor cells as measured by the frequency of the impulses in the nerve fibres derived from them. The sensation of brightness of the light falling on a man's eyes obeys, roughly, Weber's law, the smallest detectable increase in light intensity ($\triangle I$) being proportional to the intensity, I ($\triangle I/I$ is approximately constant): the overall frequency of the impulses in all the nerve fibres coming from the eyes of several different kinds of experimental animal is roughly proportional to the logarithm of the light intensity; and in certain rather simple kinds of eye found in some kinds of invertebrate animal, the frequency of the impulses in a single nerve fibre is also roughly proportional to the logarithm of the light intensity. (In some measurements of Hartline on the "king-crab" *Limulus*—a marine animal allied to the spiders—the light intensity was varied by a factor of 10,000, and each 10-fold increase in light intensity led to an increase of about 20 per second in the frequency of the impulses in a single fibre.)

As components of control systems, however, the eyes are rarely, if ever, concerned with detecting changes in general overall illumination. The misalignment which acts as their input more usually consists of a departure of the position of the image of some external object, or parts of this image, from some "desired" position on the light-sensitive surface of the eye (the *retina*): this surface consists of a mosaic of an enormous number of receptor cells, and when a misalignment occurs, certain particular cells receive more light and others receive less light. The experimental observations on which Weber's law is based are not obviously at all relevant. Nevertheless, if one considers, for example, the process of bringing a finger to some desired position by visual observation —such as an inexperienced person selecting the correct key on a typewriter—one feels subjectively that when the misalignment is large, its exact value is of no particular importance, and that a given change in the misalignment becomes increasingly important as the misalignment becomes small and the finger approaches the correct position. Something analogous to Weber's law seems to be obeyed. On the other hand, if the misalignment to be detected consists in, say, the departure of a pointer from some zero mark on a graduated scale, one does not have to judge the magnitude even of a large misalignment, since it can be related to the nearest graduation; the response/excitation relation is likely to be more nearly linear.

Receptor potentials and nerve impulse frequency. As already remarked in Chapter 2 (p. 20), stimulation of a receptor cell by the appropriate physical or chemical change in the surroundings leads, in all probability, to the appearance of a receptor potential which itself acts as a generator potential and initiates nerve impulses, or which gives rise to a separate generator potential. Receptor potentials (and generator potentials if they are different) vary in magnitude continuously with variation in the strength of the excitatory stimulus—they are not "all-or-nothing". Nerve impulses are initiated only when the receptor potential is large enough; and the larger it is the more frequently do impulses appear. There is thus a *threshold* in the excitation of a receptor cell below which the response is zero.

At the other end of the scale, when the excitatory stimuli are large, we encounter the phenomenon of *saturation;* the response reaches a limiting value which is not exceeded however large a stimulus is given. Each nerve impulse lasts an appreciable period of time: once a nerve cell has fired, it cannot fire again until the "relay" which has been actuated by the first impulse has recovered and returned to its "resting" state in which it can be triggered by the generator potential. In the most rapid "myelinated" nerves of warm-blooded animals, the maximum frequency at which impulses can occur is about 1000 per second; but in other kinds of nervous tissue, in cold-blooded animals, the maximum frequency may be less than 1 per second.

These two kinds of non-linearity, when the stimuli are very small and very large, respectively, will occur in groups or associations of receptor cells, as well as in single cells. In a group, however, different cells will reach threshold and saturation at somewhat different values of the stimulus, so that the transitions between the graded response/excitation relation in the middle of the range of stimuli, with the zero response at one end, and a constant response at the other end, will be rounded off: the complete response/excitation curve will be S-shaped.

Response/excitation relations in the "working" range. It is probable that in most living control systems the excitation of the receptors is normally above threshold and below saturation. The relation between the size of the response and the size of the stimulus, in this region, has been studied in many different kinds of receptor cell.

(1) The *stretch receptors* which occur in muscles, lying between the contractile muscle fibres, have been referred to in Chapter 3 (p. 39): they respond both to displacement (change in the length of the whole muscle) and to velocity (rate of change of length of the muscle). Measurements have been made, by different investigators, on receptors from crayfish and lobsters, and on

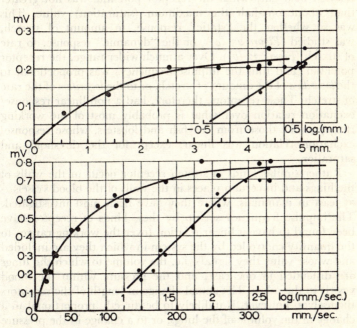

FIGURE 23 *Non-linearity in the response/excitation relation of a stretch receptor.*

A. Receptor potential (in millivolts) plotted against the *amount* of stretch (in millimetres) on linear and logarithmic scales (inset).

B. Receptor potential (in millivolts) plotted against the *rate* of stretch (in millimetres per second), on linear and logarithmic scales (inset).

The stretch receptors studies were in one of the very small muscles that move the 4th toe cf a frog.

(Re-plotted from B. Katz, 1954. Journal of Physiology, vol. 111).

receptors from frogs. Impulses are set up in the nerve fibre coming
from the receptor cells by means of a receptor potential (Chapter
2, p. 20): there is a linear relation between the impulse frequency
and the size of the receptor potential when this is above a threshold
value. A linear relation was found, also, between the amount
of stretch and the size of the receptor potential (and so also
the impulse frequency) set up by the receptors from crayfish
and lobsters, up to a saturation value reached when the muscle
was stretched by about 40 per cent of its initial length. The
receptors from frogs, however, behaved differently: the linear
relation held only when the receptor potential was not greater
than about one-half the maximum (saturation) value. This
was so whether the "static" response, to amount of stretch,
was studied (*Figure 23* (*a*)), or the "dynamic" response, to rate
of stretch (*Figure 23* (*b*)). Over a much wider range, the receptor
potential (and thus the impulse frequency) was proportional to
the *logarithm* of the amount of stretch, or to the *logarithm* of the rate
of stretch. These receptors, therefore, had a non-linear response/
excitation relation over what is probably most of the working
range, unlike those from crayfish and lobsters, whose response/
excitation relation was linear, except for the threshold and
saturation.

Rather similar kinds of stretch receptor occur in the walls of
the lungs and in certain places in the walls of the blood vessels—
at least in mammals, where they have been most investigated.
The impulse frequency set up by these kinds of receptor have
been found to have a linear relation (over the working range) to
the quantity controlled by the system in which they are included
and whose value they signal—i.e. the volume to which the lungs
are distended in one case, and the pressure within the blood
vessels in the other. The actual change in length of the receptors
themselves, however, is unlikely to be directly proportional to a
change in the volume of the lungs, or to a change in the pressure
within the blood vessels: their apparent linear properties, as
components of control systems, seems to imply non-linearity in the
receptors themselves.

(2) The receptor cells which are sensitive to the concentrations
of carbon dioxide and of oxygen in the blood (to be referred to in
Chapter 8) also have linear response/excitation relations, provided
that the threshold is exceeded.

(3) There are receptors in the tongues and skin of warm-

blooded animals which are sensitive to temperature, and which are peculiar in that the impulse frequency has a maximum value at a certain temperature and becomes smaller if the temperature is either greater or less than this. In one set of these receptors the maximum impulse frequency occurs at about 40° C and in another set it occurs at about 30° C: the important working range of the control system lies between these values. A small rise in temperature, for example, leads to a nearly proportional increase in the impulse frequency from the one set and a decrease in that from the other set: saturation occurs when the temperature rises or falls beyond the working range, but there is no threshold. Both sets of receptors respond to a positive rate of change of temperature (temperature rising) by an increase in impulse frequency and to a negative rate of change of temperature by a decrease in impulse frequency.

Effectors

In studying the response/excitation relations of the effectors, we have to consider first the relation between the mechnical or chemical force developed and the magnitude of the excitatory stimulus applied; secondly the effect on the force developed of the inherent damping, or internal velocity feedback, which comes in as soon as there is any movement of the controlled quantity at the output element; and thirdly the nature of the time delay between the beginning of the excitation and the development of the maximum force.

Force/excitation relations. The force exerted by a *muscle* can easily be measured: if its ends are not allowed to move more than is just necessary for the purpose of measuring the force, or tension, developed (which can be very small) the "contraction" is said to be *isometric*. The stimulus applied to it, as already remarked, is measured by the number of nerve fibres carrying impulses and the frequency of the impulses in each. Unless the muscle is very small, and is supplied by only a few motor nerve fibres, it is not possible to discover the number of fibres active at any moment. But each nerve fibre supplies a definite muscle fibre, or group of muscle fibres. We do not know that each of these develops the same isometric force when stimulated, but we have no reason to suppose that they are brought into action in any systematic order, as for example, the least powerful first, when only a few fibres are in action, and the most powerful last, when nearly all are in action:

unless this were so, there would be no consistent non-linearity in the relation between isometric force and number of fibres in action. There is evidence which suggests, moreover, that when a muscle is maintaining a contraction which is less than the maximum possible, and only some of its fibres need be in action at any moment, the active fibres "retire in rotation", and others are brought in to replace them. It would seem, therefore, that the relation between isometric force and number of motor fibres carrying impulses is at least approximately linear.

The force set up by a muscle increases with increase in the frequency of the stimulating nerve impulses owing to "summa-tion" of the contractions, as discussed on p. 31. The relation may be measured experimentally by artificially stimulating the motor nerve by means of pulses of electric current sufficiently large to ensure that all the fibres supplying the muscle are excited: it is definitely not linear. There is "saturation", and a maximum frequency beyond which there is no further increase in isometric force—usually considerably smaller than the maximum frequency that the nerve fibres can reach: if the frequency is zero (only one stimulus is given), some tension is set up in some kinds of muscle (the "striated" or "skeletal" muscles which move our limbs, for example), but not in others (the "unstriated" or "visceral" muscles, particularly of the "lower" invertebrates, for example—see *Figure 7*). Between these limits, the force–frequency relation is S-shaped, but there is a sensibly linear portion over nearly one-half the whole possible range of tensions. Owing to the fact that muscles can only pull and cannot push, the "motor" in many living control systems consists of a pair of muscles and the system is held at the set point as a result of both being partially excited at the same time: departures from the set point are corrected by an increased contraction of one and a decreased contraction of the other. Mostly, therefore, both muscles will be working on the linear part of the force–frequency curve, approaching "thres-hold" and "saturation" conditions only when the misalignment becomes unusually large. This, however, is not universal and in some of the living control systems the muscles must be operated by low frequencies of excitation, producing small forces, and thus work on a non-linear part of the curve.

Such experimental studies are in one respect unrealistic. The excitatory impulses reach all the muscle fibres simultaneously—or at least within a time interval which is very small compared with the duration of the contraction: normally in a whole animal, the excitations are asynchronous, excitation of some fibres being delayed with respect to that of others. Even when the frequency of excitation is small, and the interval between impulses in any one fibre is comparable with the duration of the contraction, the force developed is not jerky, as it would be with synchronous excitation, but smooth. (This, presumably, is the "object" of arranging in the nervous system that the excitation should be asynchronous.) In such circumstances, it is possible to measure the relation between isometric force developed and magnitude of the stimulus (i.e. number of fibres active and frequency of impulses in each) in terms of the integrated action potentials led off by electrodes on the surface of the muscle. In some experiments on the muscles of the calf of a man, the response/excitation relation as measured in this way was found to be linear (within the limits of experimental error) over the whole range of forces which the subject could produce, with possibly a small threshold value of excitation below which no force could be measured. The reason for the apparent discrepancy between these results and those of artificial synchronous stimulation are not known.

For a given excitation, the isometric force developed depends on the length of the muscle at which its ends are fixed. There is an "optimum" length at which a maximum force is developed: reduction to 90 per cent, or increase to 120 per cent, of the optimum length reduces the isometric force by only about 5 per cent; if the muscle is allowed to shorten further, the isometric force falls off almost linearly with reduction in length and more or less vanishes when the muscle is a quarter to half of the optimum length (depending on the kind of muscle).

Information about the response/excitation relations of *secreting and transporting cells* is very scanty. The force developed in excitation consists essentially of a local excess, or deficit, in the concentration (more strictly the "chemical potential") of the substance secreted or transported: this sets up a flow out of the cell on one side and into the cell on the other side, but its magnitude cannot be measured easily, if at all. The magnitude of the excitation will be determined either by the number of secretory nerve fibres in action and the frequency of the impulses in each, or by the concentration of some hormone in the solution surrounding the cells. Many kinds of transporting cell, however, seem to operate without any identifiable "stimulus", so that the magnitude of the excitation cannot be varied at will. It is reasonable to suppose, nevertheless, that a population of secreting or transporting cells, forming a whole gland or organ, will respond to excitation in much the same way as a population of muscle fibres.

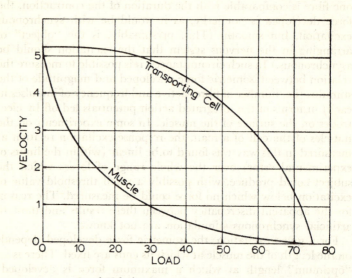

FIGURE 24   *Load-Velocity Curves for muscles and transporting cells.*

The amount of inherent damping is proportional to the slope of the line relating load to velocity. In muscles (contracting cells) it becomes smaller as v becomes greater. In transporting cells, it becomes larger as v becomes greater and eventually reaches infinity when "saturation" occurs.

For the muscle (sartorius muscle of a frog at $0°C$), the scale of ordinates shows rate of shortening in cm/sec., and the scale of abscissae shows load in grams.

For the transporting cell, the scales are arbitrary and the line is diagrammatic only.

Inherent damping. If a muscle is allowed to shorten when it is stimulated, the force produced is less than the isometric force corresponding to its length at any moment, by an amount which depends on the speed at which it moves. If a muscle is working against a load, it has to generate a force equal to that exerted by the load before any movement occurs: if this force is equal to the isometric force in response to a given excitation, there is no movement; as the opposing force becomes smaller, the speed of movement increases up to a maximum value which is reached when there is no opposing load. The relation between force and speed in every kind of muscle studied is shown in *Figure 24*. For any given muscle, there will be a "family" of curves such as that plotted in *Figure 24*, all of the same shape but with different intercepts on the axes depending on the size of the stimulus. For each size of stimulus, also, there will be another "family" of curves according to the length of the muscle when the measurements are made.

The shape of the force–velocity curve is such that when the speed is small and the force large, the curve falls steeply, a small increase in speed makes a large decrease in force, and there is a large amount of negative velocity feedback. When the speed is large, on the other hand, and the force small, the curve becomes much flatter and there is much less velocity feedback. (The slope of the line when the speed is zero is some 3 to 10 times as great, depending on the kind of muscle, as the slope when the speed is such that the force is zero.) This non-linearity of the force–velocity relation, and thus of the inherent damping of muscles, serves a useful purpose. Suppose that the input element of a servo system which has muscles as its "motor" is given a step function displacement. When the misalignment has been reduced nearly to zero, the speed of movement is small, there is considerable damping in the motor and hunting is reduced: but initially when the misalignment and speed are both large, the negative velocity feedback is smaller, the force exerted by the muscle is larger, and the misalignment is reduced more rapidly, than it would be if the damping were constant.

It has been found, similarly, that the rate at which a substance is moved from one solution to another by *transporting cells* depends on the "head" against which they have to work. This "head" is determined by the ratio of the concentrations of the substance transported in the two solutions on each side of the transporting system: if an ion is being transported with its electric charge, the "head" depends also on the electrical potential difference between the two solutions. There is a limiting "head" at which the rate of transport is zero, determined probably by the "force" generated by the transporting cells: but it may be partly determined, also, by the rate of back leakage of the substance transported either within, or between, the transporting cells. As the opposing "head" of concentration, or electrical potential, is reduced, the output of the transporting "pump" increases, at first in an approximately linear manner; a condition of "saturation" is then approached, and eventually reached, in which the output ceases to rise any more, as shown diagrammatically in *Figure 24*. Transporting cells differ from muscle (contractile) cells, therefore, in that the damping coefficient, or inherent output velocity feedback, rises as the rate of transport becomes greater, and when "saturation" is reached, the coefficient becomes infinite.

Time delays. When a muscle is suddenly excited by the arrival of a train of nerve impulses, the force developed rises gradually; when the excitation is suddenly stopped, the force falls gradually. There is thus some kind of exponential delay between stimulus and response. Without going into details, which are rather elaborate, this delay may be represented as a reasonably good approximation by two simple exponential delays: the time constants may be nearly the same, or one may be much smaller than the other, depending on the kind of muscle involved. This approximation implies that the processes within the muscle which give rise to the delay have linear properties. They are known, however, to be non-linear, and the time course of the development of force cannot be accurately represented by a combination of two, or any number of, exponential curves. The time relations of the fall in the force exerted after the stimulus ceases, may be very nearly exponential; but as a rule, the force falls more rapidly than it rises, and there is an additional source of non-linearity of a different kind. At the present stage of the study of living control systems, it is very doubtful if these non-linearities are of much importance.

Little is known about the delays associated with the onset of secretion or active transport. The rate of secretion rises gradually after the beginning of a sudden excitation, and falls gradually after the excitation stops; the delays may be considered, therefore, to be at least roughly exponential.

The nervous system and its adjustor action

As mentioned in Chapters 2 and 3, the signal sent out from a nervous system, or from some particular group of nerve cells within it, may represent the sum of several signals going into it, or the difference between them; it may depend on the rate of change of the ingoing signals, or the sum of all the signals in some past interval of time. It is not difficult to establish this in a qualitative way, but it is extremely difficult to discover quantitatively whether, and in what conditions, these mathematical operations are reasonably linear. Some evidence is available, however, from electro-physiological studies on what are probably some of the simplest kinds of operation.

As pointed out in Chapter 2 (p. 20) a nerve cell fires when a certain threshold number of impulses (n_t) arrives at the synapses within a certain period of time. In a group, or population, of cells, all of which are part of the same control system, the value of n_t varies from cell to cell over a certain range, from $(n_t)_{min}$ to $(n_t)_{max}$. Each receptor nerve fibre divides many times and sends branches to many nerve cells: and each nerve cell receives impulses from many different receptor fibres, as is indicated diagrammatically in *Figure 25*. The output from the group of nerve cells will be zero unless the stimulus is such that $(n_t)_{min}$ receptors are excited and deliver one impulse each, or that $(n_t)_{min}$ impulses are set up in a smaller number of receptor fibres within the summation time: unless $(n_t)_{min}$ is 1, the response/excitation relation will have a threshold which is greater than that of the receptors themselves. There will also be saturation when $(n_t)_{max}$ impulses arrive at the group of nerve cells. In between, the response/excitation relation is likely to be non-linear, although there may be a region in which it is approximately linear.

This, however, is the simplest case. The branches from the receptor fibres do not necessarily go directly to the nerve cells, as shown in *Figure 25*, but may go through chains of varying numbers of intermediate nerve cells, at which the impulses are delayed. It is possible, therefore, that a single impulse in each of several receptor fibres may lead to a short series of impulses from one (or several) of the "main" nerve cells, as it is excited by each of the receptor impulses after varying periods of delay. When this occurs, there will be an "amplification" of the signal at the group of nerve cells, in the sense that there is an increase in the total number of impulses in unit time. It will occur, however, only when the "excitability" of the cells is large—i.e. when the threshold number of impulses is small. Impulses may also arrive at inhibitory synapses on the nerve cells, possibly from quite distant parts of the nervous system; these will reduce the excitability and so also the "gain" in the system. Even when there is no "amplification", there may be a re-distribution of the nerve impulses: instead of being divided more or less evenly among a

D

large number of receptor fibres, they may become concentrated in a few fibres from the nerve cells. Whether, and in what way, this changes the nature of the signal is not known. Some of the chains of intermediate nerve cells may turn back on themselves, so that when the last cell fires it re-excites the first: such "regenerative" closed circuits, once started, may continue for an appreciable period of time, maintaining repetitive firing in other nerve cells and introducing delays with relatively large time constants.

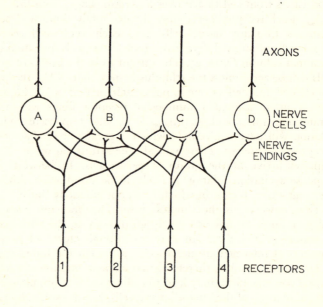

FIGURE 25   *Highly simplified diagram of the connections between receptors and nerve cells.*

For the purpose of illustration and to avoid excessive confusion, the number of nerve endings on each cell has been made equal to the threshold number of impulses necessary to fire the cell. Actually each cell will have tens or hundreds of nerve endings, and the number is not related to the threshold number of impulses.

The diagram illustrates the possibility of non-linearity in the response of the nerve cells to excitation from the receptors. If the excitatory stimulus is just sufficient to excite 1 receptor, no nerve cell will fire: if it excites 2 receptors (Nos. 3 and 4), 1 cell will fire (*D*); and if all 4 receptors are excited, all 4 cells will fire.

In the "higher", more elaborate and complicated parts of the nervous systems of most kinds of animal there appears to be a continuous traffic of "spontaneous", or random, nerve impulses, unrelated to any identifiable receptor excitation. These may arise from regenerative closed circuits of nerve cells; but it is possible, also, that some kinds of nerve cell are inherently unstable, or nearly so, a single excitation resulting in a prolonged repetitive response. It has been suggested that these impulses maintain a state of general "vigilance", as a result, perhaps, of the continuous low level excitation "taking up the slack" in the system due to the existence of thresholds.

Self-adaptive control systems

When a "conventional" servo system is put together, the gain or stiffness, and the time constants of delays, differentiating and integrating devices (the "parameters" of the system) are adjusted by the designer so that the performance of the system meets certain specifications when working in certain conditions. If these conditions—nature of input, kind of load on output, nature of disturbances acting on the output—change, the performance may become inadequate. If the system is made "self-adaptive" or "self-optimising", the parameters are made to change automatically in such a way as to restore the performance to the best value possible. A somewhat different kind of self-adaptive system is needed for a manufacturing process in which there are many different "inputs" and many different "outputs"; the "inputs", for example, may be the rate of flow, composition and temperature of each kind of raw material, the rate of supply of heat or pressure to some reaction vessel and, in addition perhaps, the conditions of the environment. All the inputs are liable to fluctuate, and on some of them it may not be possible to exert any kind of control: a system is needed, therefore, which will adjust all the others so as to maintain some optimum kind of output.

Some of the most recent work by engineers has been concerned in developing systems of this kind. They are sometimes described as "autonomic" (meaning self-governed), a word borrowed from physiologists: it defines that part of the nervous system which acts as "controller" in the regulation of the activities of the organs concerned in the circulation of the blood, digestion of the food and so forth—those which provide much of the "auxiliary machinery" essential for the more obvious "voluntary" activities of moving about, feeding, talking, thinking etc. A "philosophic physiologist" (whose name has not been preserved) is reported to have remarked that nature thought it prudent to remove these important phenomena from the caprice of an ignorant will. Actually, however, this system is not really "autonomous", but is closely linked and integrated with the other parts of the nervous system; indeed, it could not work properly otherwise.

Both kinds of self-adaptive system (which are really the same fundamentally) are non-linear in that the parameters vary with time. They need: *first*, a device for assessing the performance in terms of some "figure of merit", which may, for example, be the average value of the square of the misalignment over a suitable period of time, or some measure of efficiency such as cost per unit article manufactured or, in a transport system, quantity of fuel per unit distance travelled; *secondly*, means for comparing the figure of merit at any moment with some standard value or, more usually, with the value at some previous moment, implying a "memory" device, and showing whether the figure of merit is getting larger or smaller; *thirdly*, a device for changing the parameters of the servo system, or the magnitudes of the controllable inputs, in such a direction as to improve the figure of merit. What is done, in principle, is to arrange that the parameters, or inputs which are adjustable, increase and decrease periodically, one at a time and both together, according to a pre-set "programme" (no attempt has yet been made to deal with more than two at once). Any change which is accompanied by an increase in the figure of merit is repeated on the next cycle of the programme; other changes are omitted. Eventually all changes are accompanied by a decrease in the figure of merit and the optimum conditions have been reached. Systems which behave in this way are known, not unnaturally, as "hill-climbing" systems.

From this point of view nervous systems undoubtedly possess properties necessary for them to be self-adaptive. That many of the control systems in ourselves, particularly the more complicated ones, are of this kind is well shown by the way in which we acquire skill—in playing musical instruments, driving motor cars and so on. Living control systems quite commonly receive inputs from several different kinds of receptor and there is experimental evidence, some of which will be referred to in later chapters, that their relative importance in controlling the output may vary. With practice, a typewriter can be used correctly without looking at the keys: a control system is developed in which misalignments are detected by receptors in the joints and muscles of the arms and fingers, presumably by increasing the "gain" in these receptor systems and, since delays cannot be avoided, increasing also the error rate damping by an additional increase in the gain from rapidly adapting receptors. There is some direct evidence that such changes do occur. Tustin has studied the accuracy with which gun-layers can keep a gun pointed at a target which is given a simple harmonic motion. Analysis of the records indicated that the layers varied the size of the response to a given misalignment—i.e. the gain in the servo system—and the emphasis given to the rate of change of the misalignment—i.e. the amount of derivative control inserted—in such a way as to compensate for changes in the parameters of the mechanical control system to which they were connected.

There is plenty of evidence that memory devices are present even in quite "elementary" kinds of nervous system, although little is known about how they work. The "figure of merit" may be some assessment of the average misalignment, as, apparently, in the examples just quoted; but it may also involve more complex measures of reward and punishment, pleasure and pain or maximum "satisfaction". Changes in the parameters of the control system are brought about, presumably, by breaking existing connections between nerve cells and making new connections. Electrophysiological evidence shows that this can certainly occur, but little is known about how it is influenced by the figure of merit.

Studies of the way in which human operators act as control systems when performing rather difficult tasks, and using their eyes as misalignment detectors (as when steering a motor car) have shown that much of the output may have little or no relation to the misalignment or rate of change of misalignment: part of the control signal appears to depend on estimates, based on past experience, of what action is likely to be most appropriate. Even in Tustin's studies, the output (the motion given to the handwheel controlling the movement of the gun) was partly "random" in this sense.

In view of the extraordinary complexity of the possible kinds of "adjustor" action in the nervous system, it is perhaps surprising that it is possible to make any kind of rational analysis of living control systems. Well-established systems, however, dealing with some particular restricted activity, and in which action has become "automatic", are likely to have less bewildering complexity than those in which action is deliberate and "voluntary". The "auxiliary machinery", in particular, is subjected to less variety of input, is presented with more limited kinds of demand and has to cope with fewer disturbances than those which occur in the external world; in the ordinary course of events, at least, the self-adaptive properties of their control systems are not important. In so far as they have been studied, these systems appear to be less variable and thus, probably, less difficult to analyse than those regulating the "voluntary" activities.

6 THE PERFORMANCE OF NON-LINEAR CONTROL SYSTEMS

In living systems which are not self-adaptive, at least during the period of observation, the most important kinds of amplitude-dependent non-linearity are illustrated in *Figure 26*. The relation between the excitatory stimulus and the response evoked in a component with a linear transfer function is shown in *Figure 26 (a)*. If this component has a threshold, failing to respond at all to a

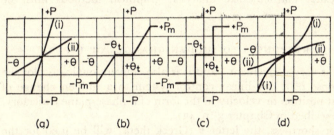

(a)   (b)   (c)   (d)

FIGURE 26 *Diagrams to illustrate various types of non-linearity.*

(*a*) The linear response/excitation relation with: (i) large "sensitivity"; and (ii) small "sensitivity" (The "ideal" component.)
(*b*) The linear relation with thresholds $\pm \theta_t$ and saturation at $\pm P_m$.
(*c*) "On-off" response.
(*d*) Non-linear response/excitation relations with: (i) "sensitivity" increasing with increase in excitation; and (ii) "sensitivity" decreasing with increase in excitation.

very small excitation, and saturates, failing to give any greater response to a greater excitation when the excitation is very large, the response-excitation relation will be as shown in *Figure 26 (b)*. In the limit, if saturation occurs immediately the threshold is reached (*Figure 26 (c)*), the component has "on-off" properties; at a certain value of the excitation, the response changes from zero to maximum (a familiar example is an electro-magnetic relay).

In living systems, the corners at each end of the region of linear response are rounded off: for small excitations above threshold, the "sensitivity" (slope of the line in *Figure 26*) rises progressively with increasing excitation until it reaches the value of the linear region; and saturation is approached by a region in which the "sensitivity" falls progressively as the excitation increases, until it becomes zero. If these regions of varying sensitivity occupy a substantial part of the working region of excitation, there will be a non-linear proportional response, as in *Figure 26 (d)*. The response of the component will be approximately proportional to some power (greater than 1) of the excitation (curve (i)) or to, say, the logarithm of the excitation (curve (ii)), as in some kinds of receptor cell.

The effects on the behaviour of linear proportional control systems of introducing thresholds and saturation, and the effects of making the proportional control non-linear, cannot be studied by exact mathematical analysis: graphical methods must be used.

RESPONSES TO SUDDEN CHANGES OF INPUT

It is very convenient—and it is also conventional—to plot the response of a non-linear control system to a sudden change of input position or velocity in the form of a phase-plane trajectory, as described in Chapter 3 (p. 43).

For shortness, the letter θ (Greek theta) will be used for the amount of misalignment in the system at any moment, and the letter v for the velocity (rate of change) of the misalignment. Similarly, θ_i and θ_o will be used for the positions of the input and output elements, and v_i and v_o for their velocities. The phase-plane trajectory is obtained by plotting θ against t at successive moments after some sudden change has been made in θ_i or v_i.

On-off control systems

We will begin by considering on-off systems, which are commonly used by engineers. (The control systems in most domestic refrigerators and in electrically heated hot-water systems are familiar examples.) Systems which have strictly on-off control are not known to occur in living organisms: but their study provides a convenient introduction to the method and the interpretation of phase-plane trajectories.

If a proportional control system saturates when the misalignment exceeds a certain value, then its behaviour in these conditions is the same as that of an on-off system when "on". If, also, there is a threshold misalignment, no signal being sent to the motor when the misalignment is less than the threshold, then in these conditions the system will behave in the same way as an on-off system when "off".

Step function input (sudden displacement). Suppose that the system is initially at rest, with input, output and misalignment all at zero. The input is then given a sudden displacement $+h$, thereby creating instantaneously a misalignment $+h$. If h is greater than the threshold, the motor is activated and the output moved in such a way that the misalignment is brought back towards zero. The phase-plane trajectory of the system, which describes its subsequent behaviour, is drawn in *Figure 27*. The threshold values at which the motor is put on (forwards or backwards) and cut off are shown by the two vertical lines, one on each side of the origin, at $\pm\theta_t$.

Most commonly, the motor and its output load will possess viscous friction and inertia: or alternatively, there may be a delay, approximately exponential, at the motor. In either case, the speed of the output element rises gradually when the motor is put on, and falls gradually after it has been cut off. This is obvious when there is inertia—a flywheel, for example, on the output element. That an exponential delay will produce the same effect may be seen by supposing that the motor is a steam engine, and that the pipe between the main steam valve and the cylinder is long and has a large diameter: if the valve is opened suddenly, the pressure at the cylinder will rise gradually as steam fills up the pipe; conversely, if the valve is shut suddenly, the engine will continue running, exerting a gradually diminishing force, until it has used up the steam in the reservoir formed by the pipe.

As the misalignment velocity increases, the misalignment itself decreases: the trajectory is thus a curve, as shown in *Figure 27*. If the motor were kept on indefinitely, the velocity of the output element, and thus also the misalignment velocity (the input velocity being zero), would approach, though never quite reach, a maximum velocity (v_m) depending on the force exerted by the motor and the coefficient of friction in the load, as is indicated by the broken line in *Figure 27*. But sooner or later, the misalignment is reduced to the threshold value, and the motor is cut off: the

D*

output does not immediately come to rest but runs on as a result of the inertia, or delay in the motor, with diminishing velocity. (By using simple mathematics, the trajectory in the dead zone can be shown to be a straight line.) Unless the velocity falls rapidly, or the initial displacement is small, the misalignment will reach the other (negative) threshold before its velocity becomes zero: the motor will reverse, the output and misalignment will first be decelerated and then accelerated in the opposite direction. The trajectory will cross the line of zero velocity and then reach the threshold again, as shown in *Figure 27*. There will be another

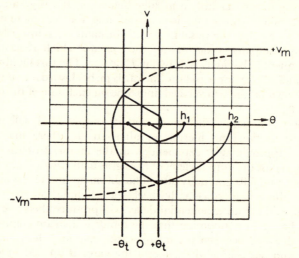

FIGURE 27   *Phase-plane trajectory of an on-off control system with inertia, or an exponential delay, and viscous friction, when the input is given a sudden displacement. (The diagram is illustrative and not strictly to scale.)*

period of falling velocity in the dead zone between the two thresholds, re-activation of the motor in the forward direction, and so on until the trajectory intersects the axis of zero velocity in the dead zone. Thus, although there is likely to be hunting, it will die away after a few cycles.

Finite delays. Suppose that the motor does not start, or stop, exerting a force precisely when the misalignment reaches the threshold value, but only after a short period of "dead time". (Electrical circuit breakers operated by electromagnets always introduce such a finite delay). When the trajectory reaches the threshold line, it continues during the dead time along its previous course, the misalignment becoming smaller and its velocity greater (more negative in the conditions of *Figure 27.*): the dead zone trajectory starts from a point closer to the $-\theta_t$ line and further from the zero velocity line than it did in the absence of the finite delay. The exact point of change-over from one part of the trajectory to the other depends on the time integral of the velocity during the dead time, and is thus not easily calculated; but it is obvious that the system is more likely to run through the dead zone, and hunt, than it would be in the absence of the finite delay.

Ramp function input. Now suppose that the input is suddenly made to move with a constant velocity (u). At the moment when the input starts to move, the misalignment velocity is the same as the input velocity, since the output has not yet started. The phase-plane trajectory thus starts at the point $\theta = 0$, $v = u$ (compare *Figure 30*, p. 102). This starting point is within the dead zone, so that the output rate (v_o) is zero. The misalignment thus rises steadily at a rate u until it becomes equal to $+\theta_t$. The output rate then increases progressively towards its maximum value (v_m), θ continuing to rise, but more slowly: when v_o becomes greater than u, the misalignment velocity becomes negative, θ falls and eventually becomes reduced to $+\theta_t$ again. As before, the output velocity now falls gradually towards zero and at some moment will become equal to the input velocity: the misalignment velocity is then zero and the trajectory crosses the axis of θ (provided that it does not cross the $-\theta_t$ line). As the output velocity continues to fall towards zero, the misalignment velocity increases towards the input velocity, but will actually reach it only after an infinite period of time. As shown in *Figure 30*, the phase-plane trajectory in the dead zone is not straight, but curls round more or less rapidly towards the line of zero velocity, which it crosses at right angles, and continues in a curve which approaches, though never reaches, the value of the input velocity. At some point on its route it crosses the threshold line at a velocity less than the input velocity; the motor is activated and the trajectory describes another loop, smaller than the first.

Eventually, the successive loops are all of the same size, and a "limit cycle" is reached, the motor being put on and cut out intermittently in such a way that it exerts an average force during each cycle just equal to the opposing force exerted by the frictional load at velocity u. It is obvious, in fact, that the motor must go into action intermittently; there is no value of the misalignment at which the output velocity can be made precisely equal to the input velocity (unless this happens to be exactly equal to the maximum output velocity). The time average of the positive and negative misalignments with respect to $+\theta_t$, however, is positive, and this corresponds to the steady state velocity error in proportional control systems, increasing with increase in the input velocity.

If the inertia, or delay, in the system is made larger, or the thresholds made smaller (to a sufficient extent), the trajectory will cross the dead zone and the motor will be reversed; the system will hunt. It cannot, however, become strictly unstable, and a limit cycle will be reached; but, particularly if there are finite delays, this may involve permanent hunting.

The effect of adding saturation and thresholds to linear proportional control systems

We will take as an example the same control system as before,

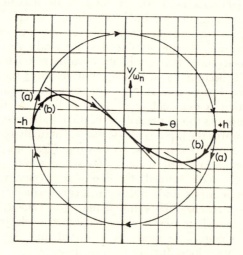

FIGURE 28   *Phase-plane trajectories of a proportional control system with inertia, or an exponential delay, given an initial displacement, h.*
(a) thin line, with no damping
(b) thick line, with output damping large enough to be critical.

with inertia, or an exponential delay, and viscous frictional damping on the output element, but with proportional control of the motor and not on-off control: it will hunt if the damping is insufficient. Suppose, to begin with, that there is no saturation or threshold.

The input is given a sudden displacement (h), and the system is released: the motor will come into action, accelerate the output and the phase-plane trajectory will start off on the same course as it had in the on-off system, and plotted in *Figure 27*. But as soon as the misalignment begins to fall, the force exerted by the motor will fall also: the output acceleration becomes smaller than it would be in an on-off system, the phase-plane trajectory flattens out and a constant velocity is reached before the misalignment is reduced to zero. It is difficult to calculate the exact shape of the trajectory, but it is easy to derive an expression which defines the slope of the trajectory as it crosses a series of lines radiating from the origin at various angles to the misalignment axis: this derivation is given in Chapter 8 (p. 176).

As pointed out in Chapter 3 (p. 43), if there is no damping, and the system oscillates continuously, the trajectory is an ellipse; this becomes a circle if the misalignment velocity is expressed in terms of the natural period of the oscillations as unit of time, as in *Figure 28 (a)*. If, on the other hand, the damping is critical and there is just no hunting, we see from *Figure 8 (b)* (p. 35, and compare pp. 40-43) that as the misalignment is brought towards zero, its velocity (slope of the line in *Figure 8*) first increases, reaches a maximum and then decreases; both misalignment and velocity of misalignment approach zero together, but never actually reach it. The phase-plane trajectory, accordingly, has the shape shown in *Figure 28 (b)*. For intermediate amounts of damping, with coefficients between 0 and 1, the trajectories will be spirals (as in *Figure 30*), overshooting the origin but gradually approaching it, each circuit representing one complete cycle of oscillation. Since the shape of the trajectory depends only on the damping coefficient, it is the same whether the damping is introduced by viscous friction, by negative output velocity feedback, or by error rate control.

Suppose now that the input is given a constant velocity (u). As in the on-off system, the phase-plane trajectory will start at the point representing $\theta = 0$ (no initial misalignment), $v = u$ (misalignment velocity is equal to input velocity). When the steady state has been reached (misalignment velocity is zero), there will be a constant misalignment, or steady state error, as was shown in Chapter 3: the trajectory will end at a point representing $\theta = \theta_s$ (the steady state error), $v = 0$. In between, it will have the same shape as before, determined by the amount of damping in the system.

Effect of saturation. If the system saturates when the misalignment exceeds some particular value, the force exerted by the motor becomes independent of the misalignment. When this occurs, the trajectory starts along a line similar to that drawn for the on-off system in *Figure 27* (*a*). The precise shape will depend on the frictional damping coefficient, on the amount of inertia or the time constant of the delay—which are the same whether saturation occurs or not—and on the maximum force exerted by the motor. This last will be less than the force which would have been exerted had there been no saturation: the output velocity will rise less rapidly, and when the misalignment falls to the critical value below which there is proportional control, the misalignment velocity will be smaller than it would have been at this value of the misalignment in the absence of saturation. This means that the misalignment will be reduced more slowly, and the whole system will take longer to settle down to an acceptable approach to the steady state. From this point of view, saturation is undesirable. But if there is any risk of the system becoming really unstable, oscillating with progressively increasing amplitude, saturation is useful, since it can be arranged to put a limit to the amplitude reached (as it does in an on-off system) and save the system from damage or destruction.

Effect of thresholds. The force exerted by the motor becomes zero when $\theta = \pm \theta_t$ (the threshold values), instead of when $\theta = 0$. If the input is given a displacement h, and the system is critically damped, it will come to rest with a misalignment of $+\theta_t$ or $-\theta_t$ according as the initial displacement was positive or negative. If the system is under-damped, the resulting trajectory will be like that drawn in *Figure 29* (*b*). In the dead zone, when θ has fallen to $+\theta_t$ (or risen to $-\theta_t$) the conditions will be the same as in an on-off system: the trajectory continues as a sloping straight line. The system comes to rest, after a number of overshoots (one positive and one negative in *Figure 29* (*b*)), with a permanent misalignment somewhere between the two thresholds, the precise value depending on the initial input displacement. In the absence of thresholds, and with the same initial misalignment (*Figure 29 (a)*) the misalignment fails to exceed $\pm\theta_t$ only after two negative overshoots and one positive overshoot. This does not mean, however, that it takes longer to reach this approximation to the steady state. Without thresholds, the time will be rather more than $1\frac{1}{2}$ natural periods: with thresholds, the time will be $1\frac{1}{4}$ natural periods *plus* the successive times taken for the dead zone to be traversed; these become longer after each successive overshoot, as the average velocity becomes smaller.

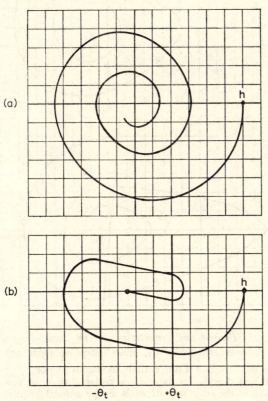

(a)

(b)

$-\theta_t$ $+\theta_t$

FIGURE 29   *Phase-plane trajectories of a proportional control system with damping coecffiient (ζ) 0.1, given an input displacement, h.*

  (*a*) without thresholds
  (*b*) with thresholds at $\pm_t\theta$.

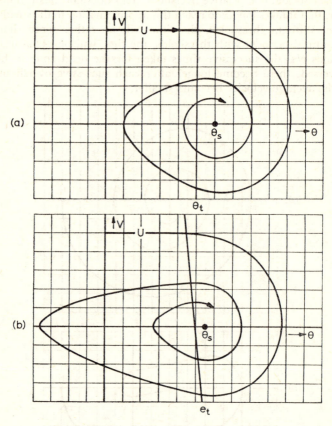

FIGURE 30 *Phase-plane trajectories of an under-damped system* ($\zeta=0.1$) *with threshold* (θ_t), *when given an input velocity u.*

(*a*) When the damping is due entirely to viscous friction.
(*b*) When half the viscous damping is replaced by error rate control.
   The shape of the trajectory depends on the natural frequency of the system: this has been taken to be 1.

When the input is suddenly given a constant velocity, instead of a displacement, the output velocity will remain at zero, and the misalignment velocity will be equal to the input velocity, until $\theta = \theta_t$. The trajectory will then have the same shape as it has in the absence of a threshold, but will be shifted to the right along the misalignment axis, ending at the point representing the sum of the steady state error (θ_s) and the threshold (θ_t). Reduction of the damping below the critical value will lead both to overshoot and to a reduction in θ_s: if the damping coefficient is sufficiently small, the trajectory will enter the dead zone and then have the same shape as it has in an on-off system (p. 97). The complete trajectory is drawn in *Figure 30* (*a*). If the input velocity is larger, or the threshold misalignment smaller, than is drawn in *Figure 30*, the trajectory will cross the dead zone and the motor will be actuated in reverse: the trajectory will continue as another portion of a spiral until it reaches the $-\theta_t$ threshold line again.

The trajectory is changed if error rate control is used. The force exerted by the motor now depends on the sum of a term proportional to the misalignment and a term proportional to the rate of change (velocity) of the misalignment, or on a quantity which is often known as the "control signal". Since initially the misalignment velocity is equal to the input velocity, there will be a control signal, and the motor will be activated, even when the misalignment itself is less than the threshold value. Moreover, if, for example, the amount of viscous damping is reduced when error rate control is added so as to keep the damping coefficient unchanged, the steady state error will be reduced. The whole trajectory is thus shifted to the left. In the presence of error rate control, the threshold lines, as shown in *Figure 30* (*b*), must be drawn sloping downwards from left to right, passing through zero misalignment when the velocity signal is equal to the threshold value of the control signal (positive or negative), and through zero misalignment velocity when the misalignment signal is equal to the threshold. This, of course, applies also when the input is given a sudden displacement. Damping by error rate control is ineffective in the dead zone, when the control signal is too small to activate the motor. The misalignment velocity will fall more slowly than it would if the damping were due entirely to viscous friction, and the misalignment will fluctuate more widely.

Similarly, when there is negative output velocity feedback, the control signal will include a term proportional to the output velocity. The threshold lines will again slope downwards from left to right: but initially the output velocity is zero, and the control signal is equal to the misalignment signal. The threshold line will pass through the misalignment threshold when the misalignment velocity is equal to the input velocity—i.e. the trajectory will start to curve downwards when the misalignment is at the threshold value. When the misalignment velocity is zero, the output velocity is equal to the input velocity: the control signal will be zero (at its threshold value) when the misalignment signal is greater than its threshold by an amount equal to the velocity signal. In effect, this means that the sloping threshold lines will be shifted upwards by an amount equal to the input velocity. Output velocity feedback, when added deliberately, will be absent in the dead zone, as is error rate control: but when it is due to an inherent property of the motor, it may be present.

With proportional control it is always possible to find a value of the misalignment, θ (the steady state value) at which the motor just exerts the correct force to keep the output velocity equal to the input velocity. If the damping is small (as in *Figure 30*) the amplitude of the oscillations (the fluctuations in θ) may well be such that at first θ periodically falls below the threshold (of the control signal if this differs from the misalignment signal) so that the motor comes into action intermittently, as it does in an on-off system, possibly in alternate directions. But unless the system is actually unstable, the intermittent activity of the motor will eventually be replaced by steady operation.

Unstable systems and limit cycles

The proportional control systems so far discussed will not become unstable in the sense of going into oscillation with a progressively increasing amplitude. More elaborate systems with, for example, complex or finite delays may become unstable: if any of their components saturate, or have thresholds, the amplitude of the oscillations increases only to a limiting value. The effect of a saturating component will be discussed in the latter part of this chapter: the effect of a threshold will be illustrated by drawing the phase-plane trajectory of an unstable system.

As pointed out at the end of Chapter 3, it is difficult, or impossible, to solve the transfer functions of complicated servo systems, and thus to discover the time course of the misalignment after the input has suddenly been given a displacement or a velocity: it is thus difficult or impossible to draw the phase-plane trajectories of such systems. By using a graphical method, however, it is easy to draw one for a system which has proportional control, output damping and a finite delay, instead of the exponential delay considered previously: as shown in Chapter 4, such a system may be unstable. The procedure is described in Chapter 8. In this example, the input is supposed to be suddenly given a constant velocity, and the resulting phase-plane trajectories, with or

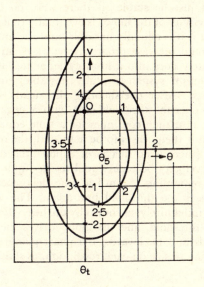

FIGURE 31   *Phase-plane trajectories of a simple servo system with a finite delay.*

Entire curve: without threshold; the system is unstable.
Inner loop: with threshold and dead zone, a limit cycle is reached.
The numbers on the trajectories indicate time intervals. (See also *Figure 39*, p. 178).

without a threshold, are drawn in *Figure 31*. Only one (positive) threshold has been inserted: it is assumed that the misalignment cannot become negative and that the motor is never reversed. This is not uncommon in living control systems. An animal, for example, consumes oxygen and produces carbon dioxide: the rate of intake of oxygen from its surroundings, and the rate of discharge of carbon dioxide, are adjusted so as to be equal to the rate of consumption of the one and the rate of production of the other, the misalignment being the total quantity of oxygen, or carbon dioxide, in the animal at any moment. This system will be discussed in more detail in Chapter 7.

As with the system with an exponential delay, the phase-plane trajectory enters the dead zone only when the delay time is so long, the frictional damping is so small, or the stiffness is so large, that the whole system is very nearly unstable. Even so, provided that it would just be stable (if there were no threshold) the intermittent activity of the motor is eventually replaced by steady operation. But if it is actually unstable, and the amplitude of the oscillations would increase progressively, a system with a threshold immediately goes into a limit cycle, as if it were an on-off system. (An on-off system is really unstable, since it has an infinite stiffness.) After overshooting the steady state position, the trajectory cuts the threshold line with a negative misalignment velocity, and then continues for a time equal to the finite delay: the motor then ceases to be activated, the output velocity becomes zero (there is no inertia or exponential delay) and the misalignment velocity becomes equal to the input velocity, as it was initially, remaining so until a time delay period after the trajectory crosses the threshold line again. The whole cycle is then repeated indefinitely, as shown by the heavy line in *Figure 31*. If there is no threshold, and the motor drives the system alternately forwards and backwards, the phase-plane trajectory is a spiral, increasing in size on each revolution, as shown by the thin line in *Figure 31*.

Non-linear proportional control systems

As pointed out at the beginning of this chapter, it is rare in living systems to find sudden and discontinuous transitions between a dead zone and a region of proportional control, or between proportional control and saturation: the gain, or stiffness, does not rise suddenly from zero to a constant value, or fall suddenly from this value to zero again. In the transitional regions, the relation between the force exerted by the motor and the misalignment may be represented by curves such a those marked (*i*) and (*ii*) in *Figure 26 (d)*.

This diagram, however, gives an incomplete and simplified picture of the situation. In many control systems there is negative output velocity feedback and error rate control, and the factors by which the output, or misalignment, velocity are multiplied before they are subtracted or added to the misalignment— hitherto expressed as "time constants"—may not be constant: they may introduce non-linearity into the system even when the simple misalignment control is linear. In order to allow for both these sources of non-linearity, we suppose that the force exerted by the motor depends on the "control signal", denoted by e, as defined on p. 103 above. In a linear system the force is directly proportional to the control signal—i.e. equal to $K.e$: in a non-linear system it is proportional to some perhaps complicated function of e—as already remarked, it might, for example, be equal to $K.e^n$, where n is greater than 1, in the region just beyond the threshold; or equal to $K.\log e$ when saturation is being approached. The phase-plane trajectory of such a non-linear proportional control system can be drawn by means of a graphical construction, which needs mathematics for adequate explanation: it is described in Chapter 8.

The effect of the non-linearity on the performance of the servo system can be seen qualitatively, however, without actually drawing the phase-plane trajectory. The most interesting and important condition is that in which the force exerted by the motor rises more than in direct proportion to the control signal—if, say, doubling the signal increases the force by a factor of three or four. Such a condition will occur, for example, when the misalignment is signalled by a receptor system which contains a large number of receptor cells with different thresholds, so that as the misalignment increases, not only does each cell fire more frequently, but the number of cells firing increases also. The consequence of the increase in gain in the system with increase in the misalignment is that the output element is accelerated more rapidly, and attains a greater velocity than it would otherwise do: the steady state position is reached more rapidly. It is possible, indeed, with such a system that the time taken to get within an acceptable distance of the steady state actually becomes smaller as the initial input displacement is made larger. But if the gain in a linear system were increased to the same extent, the damping would be reduced and the system would hunt more seriously or become actually unstable. In the non-linear system this is avoided since the gain automatically becomes reduced, and the damping increased, as the steady state is approached. Such a non-linear system thus has the best of both worlds—a rapid response without undue hunting or instability. The same effect is produced by the non-linear force-velocity relation of a muscle: now, however, the damping is reduced by a reduction in the amount of velocity feedback, as already pointed out (p. 85), rather than by an increase in the gain.

The other kind of non-linearity—that which is introduced, for example, by the logarithmic relation between stimulus and rate of firing found in some kinds of receptor, or the "force-velocity" relation of a secreting gland—will have much the same effect on the behaviour of the servo system as the introduction of saturation, already discussed. The change from saturation to proportional control, however, will be gradual, instead of sudden. The logarithmic kind of non-linearity does not seem to have any obvious advantage over a linear system with saturation. It will, however, counteract the opposite kind of non-linearity if they occur in the same system, with the result that the whole will behave in a more nearly linear manner. But we know too little about the matter to say whether this is of any value or not.

RESPONSES TO SIMPLE HARMONIC INPUTS

As described in Chapter 4, the response of a servo system when its input is given an oscillating (simple harmonic) motion is represented graphically in the form of a Nyqvist diagram, or an attenuation and phase plot. When this is done, it is assumed that the amplitude of the output is directly proportional to the amplitude of the misalignment, so that when the ratio of the one to the other is plotted against frequency, the resulting curve is characteristic of the system, whether the amplitudes are large or small. This is no longer true when one or more components in the system behave in a non-linear way.

Suppose that we apply a simple harmonic motion to a system in which the relation between output and input is represented by a curve such as one of those drawn in *Figure 26* (*d*). The first point to note is that the motion of the output element will be distorted, and will no longer be simple harmonic. As may be seen by comparing *Figure 26* (*d*) with *Figure 26* (*a*), if the non-linearity is represented by curve (i), the peaks of the waves in the output motion will be extended and sharpened: if it is represented by curve (ii), the peaks will be flattened, and in the limit, if the input motion is such that saturation is reached, they will be cut off altogether. Now there is a mathematical theorem (Fourier's theorem) which states that any wave-form, of whatever shape, may be constructed by adding together a sufficiently large number of simple harmonic motions with different frequencies and different amplitudes. The effect of the non-linearity in distorting the motion of the output element, therefore, is to add to the simple harmonic motion with the "fundamental" frequency (applied to the input element), a large number of simple harmonic motions with greater frequencies and, in general, smaller amplitudes. In all servo systems considered so far, the output/misalignment ratio falls—the attenuations becomes increasingly negative—as the frequency rises: and this is true, also, even in more complicated systems unless there is a large proportion of derivative (phase advance) control. (This is primarily due to the effects of friction and inertia in the output element.) The "spurious" high frequency components introduced by the non-linearity are present in the force exerted by the motor, but their effects on the output *position* are small compared with those of the fundamental frequency, and can usually be ignored. Their existence, however, is a clear indication of the presence of non-linearities in one or more components of the control system.

The second, and more important, point to note is that the amplitude of the output is no longer directly proportional to the amplitude of the input, or misalignment: if the system saturates, for example, increasing the misalignment amplitude beyond a certain value will have little or no effect on the output amplitude. The non-linearity, moreover, may be in some frequency-dependent component, such as the amount of output velocity feedback, or derivative control. Both the output/misalignment amplitude ratio, and the output–misalignment phase difference may vary with the misalignment amplitude, and the behaviour of the system cannot be described completely by a single transfer locus (Nyqvist diagram, or attenuation-phase plot, for example).

The Describing Function

In order to calculate the output from a non-linear component (of the kind that we are now considering) we must multiply its input by some quantity which itself varies with the input. The particular form, or nature, of this variation is a description of the way in which the non-linearity behaves. It is thus called the "Describing Function", which is a kind of transfer function for the non-linearity. As a simple example, the Describing Function of a component which acts in a linear manner so long as its input is less than a certain size, and then saturates, is 1 when the input is below the critical value, and then falls progressively towards 0 which it would reach if the input were infinitely large. The Describing Function and its reciprocal, the "Inverse Describing Function" (see p. 113 below) are plotted in *Figure 41* (Chapter 8, p. 183) for a saturating component and for a component with a "cubic characteristic" imitating the type of non-linearity illustrated in *Figure 26* (*d*) (i).

Graphical construction of the frequency response of a non-linear system

All the components of the system, except one, are assumed to behave in a linear manner, and all the non-linear behaviour is lumped together in this one remaining component: the block diagram of the system is shown in *Figure 32*. It is convenient,

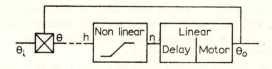

FIGURE 32   *Block diagram of a simple servo system containing a non-linear component.*

though not essential, to suppose that all the linear components are placed between the non-linear component and the output element: it makes no difference to the behaviour of the system in what order they are arranged. An input of some desired frequency is given and the signal is observed as it leaves the non-linear component; it is marked n in *Figure 32*, has an amplitude written as $|n|$ and is considered to have zero phase angle.

(1) The amplitude of the signal entering the non-linear component ($|h|$), and its phase angle can be calculated from the Describing Function of the component. (It is not essential to have this in the form of an algebraic equation; it is sufficient if it is in the form of a graph, as measured experimentally, for example.) For simplicity it will be assumed that the non-linear component does not introduce any change of phase, so that the phase of the signal h is also zero. (If there is a change of phase which depends

on the amplitude of h, the analysis becomes more difficult, but is not impossible.)

(2) The signal n goes to the motor, through the intervening components, and appears as the output motion (θ_o). The amplitude and phase of θ_o is found from the known properties of these linear components and the nature of the output load. For example, if there is an exponential delay and a viscous load, the amplitude and phase of θ_o (in terms of the amplitude and phase of the signal n, taken as 1 and 0 respectively) can be read from *Figure 14 (c)* (p. 51). It is necessary to know the natural frequency of the system, which can be calculated from the stiffness, the coefficient of viscous friction and the time constant of the delay (see Chapter 8). The line drawn in *Figure 14 (c)* gives the amplitude and phase of θ_o when the input frequency is 0.8 times the natural frequency. If, in addition, there is error rate control, the change in amplitude and phase can be read from *Figure 20*.

(3) The output motion is fed back to the misalignment detector where it is subtracted from the input motion (θ_i) to give the misalignment signal (θ). Since the system has been arranged so that there are no components between the misalignment detector and the non-linear component, the signal θ is the same as the signal h, whose phase angle is assumed to be zero. The problem, therefore, is to find the amplitude and phase of the input motion which will give rise to a misalignment signal with amplitude $|h|$ (as discovered by the use of the Describing Function) and zero phase angle.

(4) By using a simple graphical construction (given in Chapter 8, pp. 182-184) it is possible to find a whole range of input signals, with different amplitudes but each with its appropriate phase angle, which will give misalignment signals with zero phase angle but, of course, different amplitudes. Several of these input signals are chosen, each with a different amplitude $|\theta_i|$, and for each the value of $|n|/|\theta_i|$ is plotted against the corresponding value of $|h|/|\theta_i|$ $(=|\theta|/|\theta_i|)$. By repeating the whole series of computations using different frequencies for the signals studied, a family of these curves is obtained. These define the behaviour of the linear components of the system.

(5) On the same chart curves are plotted showing the relation between $|n|/|\theta_i|$ and $|h|/|\theta_i|$ which define the behaviour of the non-linear component as obtained from the Describing Function. There will be a family of these for different values of the input

amplitude $|\theta_i|$. (For example, if the non-linear component saturates when its input exceeds some value h_c, then the relation between $|n|$ and $|h|$ will depend on whether $|\theta_i|$ is such that $|h|$ is greater or less than h_c, and on the amount by which $|h|$ exceeds h_c.)

(6) Each point of intersection between a "linear" curve and a "non-linear" curve defines the operating conditions for some particular frequency and some particular input amplitude. Consider the points at some constant input amplitude but different frequencies: each defines a value of $|n|$, from which the amplitude and phase of θ_o can be obtained (para. (2) above). From the selected values of $|\theta_i|$ the phase of θ_i at each frequency is known (para (4) above). The overall (closed loop) transfer locus can thus be plotted. This, however, does not completely describe the behaviour of the system. The whole process must be repeated using different values of $|\theta_i|$ and a family of transfer loci plotted.

Complete analysis of the frequency response of a non-linear system is a very laborious process and is not often worth the effort involved. With living systems it might, however, be of some value to use the graphical method in reverse. It might be possible to measure the overall frequency response of some complete control system over a wide range of input amplitudes. If the properties of the linear components were known—or assumed to be defined by the frequency response when the input was very small—the Describing Function of the non-linear components could be discovered.

Stability of a non-linear system

According to the Nyqvist criterion (Chapter 4, p. 61) a system will oscillate with progressively increasing amplitude if the open loop frequency response (transfer) locus crosses the negative real axis beyond the point $(-1, j.0)$—i.e. leaves this point on its right when we proceed in the direction of increasing frequency. Suppose, for example, that it passes through the point $(-2, j.0)$: this means that when the frequency is such that the output is just out of phase with the misalignment, the output amplitude is twice the misalignment amplitude. If the loop were closed, any small misalignment that may arise will pass round the loop unchanged in phase, and increasing in amplitude on each circuit. Suppose, now, that a saturating component is inserted somewhere in the loop. So long as the amplitude of the oscillation is less than the critical amplitude for saturation, it will have no effect: larger oscillations will be reduced in amplitude as they pass through it. At some value of the amplitude of the input to the saturating component (h in *Figure 32*), the output from it (n) will be reduced by a factor (2 in the illustrative example) equal to the dynamic magnification in the remainder of the system: the whole system will then oscillate with a constant amplitude, and it will never become strictly unstable.

In general, this limiting amplitude is most easily found by plotting the Inverse Describing Function (that is the value of $-|h|$ for given values of $|n|$ as shown, for example in *Figure 41*) on the same chart as the loop transfer locus. The plot will start at the point $(-1, j.0)$ for very small values of $|h|$ (when the non-linearity is negligible), and if there is no phase change in the non-linear component, all the other points will lie on the negative real axis, spaced unevenly, beyond the point $(-1, j.0)$. The point at which the transfer locus crosses the Inverse Describing Function locus gives the value of $|h|$ for stable oscillation. From this, we can find $|\theta|$ ($|\theta| = |h|$ in the system illustrated in *Figure 32*) and hence $|\theta_o|$ the amplitude of the output oscillations.

If the non-linear component, on the other hand, were of the opposite kind, in which the ratio of $|n|$ to $|h|$ increases as $|h|$ becomes larger, there will be some value of the input amplitude at which the system is just unstable. This value can be discovered, similarly, by superimposing a plot of the Inverse Describing Function on the loop transfer locus of the system in the absence of the non-linear component.

Behaviour of non-linear systems when given inputs of complicated waveforms

One of the difficulties in analysing the behaviour of non-linear systems is the failure of the "superposition rule". The response of a linear system to any kind of oscillating input can be derived by superposing its responses to the simple harmonic motions of all the various frequencies and amplitudes which, when combined, make up the input motion (as discovered by Fourier analysis): this is not true when the system is non-linear. It would be beyond the scope of this book to do more than just mention some of the methods which can be used to overcome this difficulty, at least in part; the mathematics involved may be quite advanced. One method is to use as input to the system an oscillation consisting of two simple harmonic motions of different frequency and amplitude. We then have to find the "dual input describing function" of the non-linear component—i.e. a relation which describes its behaviour when supplied with two inputs simultaneously: this can be done analytically only with certain kinds of non-linearity, and experimental methods are usually necessary.

A procedure which may prove to be useful when studying living systems is to give the system an input of some desired frequency and to find its output. The loop is then opened just before the non-linear component (assuming that there is only one) and a signal injected at the break, of such an amplitude that the output is the same as it was when the loop was closed. Another signal, of different amplitude and frequency, is then added to this signal, and the output at this frequency observed. In effect, therefore, the loop is closed as far as what we may call the "main" signal is concerned, but open in respect of the "subsidiary" signal. In this way we can discover the "incremental" Nyqvist diagram. Such a procedure has proved useful in studying several peculiarities found in the frequency responses of non-linear systems.

Study of the behaviour of a control system when supplied with several superposed simple harmonic motions leads, in the limit, to the study of its behaviour when supplied with an infinite number of such signals, combining to form a random input or "noise". It is more useful in practice, however, to adjust the range of frequencies and amplitudes in the test input to imitate those in the inputs and disturbances which the system is likely to receive when in use. Failure of the superposition rule is now of no consequence. Such an input cannot be described by any simple algebraic expression, such as that for a simple harmonic motion; it must be described in terms of the probability that over any small interval of time δt, the amplitude will lie between some value χ and a very slightly greater value $\chi + \delta\chi$. Analysis of the behaviour of the system to such inputs is too difficult to be dealt with here. One point, however, is fairly obvious: any "resonance" effects, or frequencies at which the dynamic magnification is particularly large, will be easily detected. These may not be the same as those detected by the simple frequency response method, and may well be important in the design of the system.

7 THE PROPERTIES OF SOME LIVING CONTROL SYSTEMS

In discussing the evidence for the constancy of the internal environment, Claude Bernard (and Barcroft and Cannon after him) considered its content of water, oxygen, carbon dioxide and other substances used or produced by the living chemical factories; its content of mineral salts; and its temperature. A homeostatic control system is responsible for regulating the exchange of each of these substances, and of heat, with the external world. Each has its receptors and its effectors, hidden for the most part within the animal (or plant): and only rarely are their activities apparent to an external observer (or, by analogy with ourselves, to the animal itself) unless looked for specially. In addition, there are many other control systems, less obviously concerned in homeostasis, but just as important.

There would be little value in maintaining the internal environment constant unless an animal were able to seek out its food, hunt its prey and avoid damage from inanimate objects or its enemies. Control systems regulate the position and movement of the parts of the whole animal (and, to a smaller extent, of the whole plant) with respect to the surroundings: movements are brought about, and positions maintained, in animals by the action of muscles on the parts of the skeleton to which they are attached, whether this skeleton is internal, as in the "common or ordinary" vertebrate animals, or external as in lobsters and such like and in insects; and the muscles are controlled, for the most part, according to information about the external world derived from the "distance receptors" (eyes, ears, nose). (An example of this kind of control system in man is the one responsible for "eye-hand co-ordination" referred to in Chapter 5.)

Plants also have their relations with the external world; "ordinary" plants, for example, would be in a poor way unless their roots grew downwards, into the ground, and their stems and shoots grew upwards, into the air and light. They have control systems which ensure this, and other more detailed kinds of posture, as well as systems which, for example, regulate flowering, pollination, distribution of seeds, and so on.

None of these control systems could work unless the effector cells had an adequate supply of fuel to provide a source of power. The rate at which fuel is used, and waste products produced, moreover, (the "metabolic rate" as it is called) may vary very considerably from time to time, and according to circumstances: skeletal muscles, for example, when active may have a metabolic rate some hundred of times greater than it is when they are at rest. (Receptors and the nervous system, like all living cells, also need a supply of fuel for "maintenance", but this is relatively small and constant.) In all but the most primitive kinds of animal—such as sea anemones and some kinds of worm—the supply of fuel depends on the circulation of the blood. The effector cells which act as "motors" of the systems controlling the composition of the internal environment, moreover, are localised in certain parts of the animal; the receptors which act as misalignment detectors may be in some different part; and the inputs to the systems may arise from the activities of cells in various parts. The blood provides the essential transport between them. It would obviously be uneconomic to maintain the maximum rate of blood flow to every cell in the animal whether it needed it or not; instead, the flow is adjusted appropriately by means of control systems. Plants also have transport systems, but control of the rate of flow is less obvious than it is in animals, and less is known about it.

CONTROL OF MUSCULAR MOVEMENTS

The "stretch reflex"

When an animal's limb, or part of it, is moved "passively" by an observer or by contact with some inanimate object, one at least of the muscles attached to its bones will be stretched. The stretch receptors within it, as already mentioned more than once, will generate nerve impulses which travel along the "sensory" or "afferent" nerve fibres to the nervous system. Here they may take many different paths of varying degrees of complexity; but the one that we are now concerned with, the simplest, consists of a direct synaptic junction with "motor" nerve cells. When one of these fires in response to impulses from some particular stretch receptor, it sends nerve impulses to muscle fibres in close proximity to that receptor: these fibres are excited, become shorter, and restore the limb to its previous position, removing the stimulus to the stretch receptor. Alternatively, if the displacement of the limb is to be maintained, a force must be applied adequate to overcome the force exerted by the muscles. This "stretch reflex" is a position control system which is the basis of the control of posture and movement. It is quite independent of feeling or consciousness (though it can be modified, or over-ridden, by "voluntary" action), and, indeed, is best studied in experimental animals from whom all the "higher" parts of the brain have been removed. The stretch reflex may then become greatly exaggerated: engineers would describe the effect as that of a great increase in the gain of the control system; physiologists who have observed how difficult it is to move, passively, a limb in such a condition of "decerebrate rigidity" will appreciate the use of "stiffness" as an alternative word.

A man, or any other animal, can remain in a standing position, whether on two legs or four, only by the unremitting activity of his muscles and the servo systems controlling them. When this ceases, the joints in his legs fold up and he collapses to the ground. At each joint there are two main sets of muscles, one of which, the "flexors", makes the joint fold up, and the other, the "extensors", straightens it out; whenever a joint begins to bend or fold up, the extensor muscles are stretched. The standing position, therefore, might be maintained by allowing the joints to fold until the extensor muscles were so stretched that, as a result of the stretch reflex, they exerted sufficient force just to oppose that exerted by the weight of the animal. A steady state like this, however, is not as a rule maintained for very long. A standing animal is like a box balanced on four walking-sticks, each jointed in the middle; to represent a man, the box is up-ended and balanced on two such jointed sticks. So long as the arrangement is, in fact, balanced, no muscular activity is necessary: but it is a highly unstable condition, maintained by intermittent momentary activity in whatever muscles are appropriate to restoring the system from any direction in which it is tending to topple over. Such intermittent activity can be detected by recording the electric changes in the muscles.

At first sight, it would seem likely that the control systems involved would hunt badly. No misalignment signals will appear in the system until the joints have folded so far that the threshold of the stretch receptors has been exceeded. The force tending to make the joints fold up increases rapidly as the system departs from the position of balance, so that the muscles must exert a correspondingly large opposing force as soon as any misalignment signal arises. The stretch receptors will be excited by the rate of stretch even more than by the amount of stretch and will immediately generate a fairly large signal: indeed, the whole system will behave nearly in an on-off manner. The system possesses appreciable inertia also (as well as finite delays) and is likely to overshoot the dead-zone about the position of balance. The instability, however, is less marked than might be expected, because the system is more elaborate than this: other receptors besides the stretch receptors take part, and the threshold of the stretch receptors themselves may be reduced by the presence of "bias" applied to them, as will be described later. The other receptors are in the joints themselves; the soles of the feet, signalling variations in the distribution of the pressure on the ground; in the "semi-circular canals" in the head, signalling angular velocity in the three planes of space; and above all, in the eyes, particularly in man. With his eyes, the animal or man detects quite small changes in the relative positions of objects in space, consequent on small shifts of the position of his head from that corresponding to correct balance. A standing man, even with his eyes open, sways slightly to and fro and from side to side: on shutting his eyes the amplitude of the sway usually increases considerably. A permanently blind man, however, manages perfectly well on the remaining control systems—an instance of their "self-adaptive" properties similar to those mentioned in Chapter 5.

The stretch reflex servo system. In terms of a simple servo system, as represented in the block diagram of *Figure 1*, a departure from the position of balance constitutes a "disturbance" applied to the output element, and fed back to the misalignment detector (the stretch receptors). In these conditions, the input to the system is zero or constant, and the control signal activating the motor (the muscle fibres) depends only on the disturbing signal. The properties of the system may be studied in an experimental animal from which the whole brain has been removed under an anaesthetic. One of the muscles of a hindleg is attached to a device which stretches it by a few millimetres, either suddenly (by a step function) or rhythmically at any desired frequency. The misalignment signal from the stretch receptors may be measured by recording the electrical changes (action potentials) in one or a few nerve fibres running from the muscle to the spinal cord (the only part of the nervous system remaining): the control signal activating the muscle fibres may be measured by recording the electrical changes appearing at electrodes inserted among them; and the force exerted by the contracting muscles may be measured in terms of the force applied by the stretching device. Since the muscle is rigidly attached to the mechanical stretching device, the movement of the output element is independent of the activity of the motor (contractions of the muscle), so that the servo loop has effectively been opened.

The results of such measurements as have been made are not very consistent or easy to interpret. The system is undoubtedly non-linear, but the nature of the non-linearities has not been adequately investigated: and its properties may vary from time to time in an unpredictable manner. When the muscle is given a sudden stretch, there is a finite delay (of about $\frac{7}{1000}$ secs. in a cat) before the control signal (action potentials) appears in the muscle: this corresponds with the time taken by a nerve impulse to travel from a stretch receptor to the spinal cord, across a synapse and back again to a muscle fibre. When the muscle is stretched rhythmically at any given frequency, this finite delay will introduce a phase lag between stretch and excitation of muscles, the phase angle becoming increasingly negative as the frequency is made greater (compare *Figures 18* and *19*, pp. 62, 63). There will be a further delay between the excitation of the muscles and the development of maximum tension, which will increase the angle of phase lag. The magnitude of this delay will depend on whether the muscles are being stretched by the mechanical device at the moment of excitation, or are being allowed to shorten.

The misalignment signal (action potentials in the receptor nerves) is found to be in phase with the stretch—depending on the change in length of the muscles—at zero and very low frequencies; and becomes progressively more advanced in phase, depending on the rate of change of length, as the frequency is made greater. This is what would be expected from the properties of the stretch receptors described in Chapters 3 and 5. The phase angle, however, some $+40°$ at 1 cycle per second, reaches $+90°$ at about 7 c/s, less than 3 octaves greater—a larger change than is given even by an "ideal" differentiating system (compare *Figure 20*).

E

At low frequencies, less than a few cycles per second, this phase advance is more than sufficient to annul the phase lag introduced by the delays, and the force exerted by the contracting muscles reaches a maximum value in advance of the maximum increase in length. (There may also be some further phase advance introduced in the nervous system.) At higher frequencies, however, this is not so: the delays may be such that the muscle begins to contract at the moment of maximum length and is just fully contracted at the moment of minimum length, half a cycle later. The activity of the muscle is then just in phase with the movements of the stretching device and there is a kind of resonance between them. If the stretching device is replaced by a simple spring and the muscle given an initial stretch, the stretch receptors will be excited, the muscle will contract after a certain delay, remove the stretch and the excitation of the receptors, be stretched again by the spring, and so on, oscillating at about the "resonant" frequency. There is experimental evidence that such periodic activity may occur in the muscles of experimental animals, the frequency in a cat being 12–16 c/s: it has also been observed in human muscles during "voluntary" contractions, the frequency being 9–10 c/s, in accordance with the fact that the finite delay between stretch receptor excitation and muscle fibre excitation is about 30 milliseconds instead of 7 milliseconds. Ordinarily these oscillations are of small amplitude and are not apparent without special methods of investigation. But in certain diseased conditions they may become so large as seriously to affect the control of muscular movement.

The follow-up servo system in skeletal muscles

So far the stretch reflex servo system has been considered in its simplest condition, with zero or constant input and responding to disturbance applied to the output. But it may also be given an independent input. The stretch receptors lie on a fibre, more or less in the middle, whose ends are attached to the same parts of the skeleton as are the muscle fibres, as shown diagrammatically in *Figure 33*: in the mammals the whole structure containing the receptors has the shape of a spindle, and the stretch receptors are sometimes called "spindle receptors". Except in the part where the receptors are attached, this fibre is a muscle fibre and thus capable of shortening when excited. When this occurs, the receptor portion of the fibre is stretched and the receptors excited, just as if the whole muscle were stretched. These "intrafusal" (within the spindle) muscle fibres are supplied by quite a different set of nerve fibres from those supplying the "extrafusal" or "main" muscle fibres. In experimental animals it is possible, though not very easy, to record the impulses in the "fusimotor" nerves separately from those in the "main" motor nerves. If, for example, the skin is touched lightly, impulses are set up in the fusimotor nerves and presumably the intrafusal muscle fibres contract: certainly,

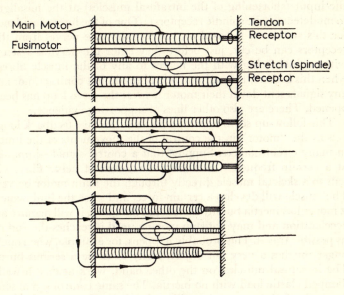

FIGURE 33   *The stretch-reflex follow-up system.*

Diagrams (highly simplified) showing a muscle "spindle" with stretch receptors and intrafusal muscle fibre, lying between the extrafusal, or "main" muscle fibres with receptors on their tendons; and the nerve fibres supplying them.

Actually, a spindle contains many muscle fibres, each with a set of stretch receptors, with somewhat different structures and modes of action: the nerve endings are all much more elaborate than is shown; and there are many more than two main muscle fibres to each spindle.

Top: system at rest;

Middle: fusimotor nerves excited, intrafusal muscles shorten and stretch receptors excited; no change in length of whole system;

Bottom: main motor nerves excited reflexly ("stretch reflex"), main muscle fibres shorten, spindle restored to original length and stretch receptors silent.

impulses appear in the afferent (sensory) fibres coming from the stretch receptors even when no change in the length of the whole muscle, or activity in the main muscle fibres, can be detected. These impulses travel to the nervous system, impulses travel back in the main motor nerves, the main muscle fibres contract and the receptor parts of the spindles return to their original lengths. The whole arrangement is essentially a follow-up servo system: the output (shortening of the main muscles) is subtracted from the input (shortening of the intrafusal muscles) at the misalignment detector (the spindle receptors). (One of the lines of evidence for this statement is based on the fact that the nerves from the receptors can be cut, just before they enter the nervous system, without interfering with the nerves to any of the muscle fibres: when this is done, the main muscle fibres do not contract, nor are any signals sent down their motor nerves; the servo loop has been opened. There are also other lines of supporting evidence.)

This follow-up servo system, with its subsidiary feedback loop, acts as the "motor" in the control of the movements of the limbs in many circumstances. Suppose that a control signal—impulses at a certain frequency in a certain number of nerve fibres—is sent to a skeletal muscle directly through the main motor nerves. The muscle will develop a certain force, and since the limb which it moves has inertia but little frictional damping, it will acquire an acceleration and may not stop moving until it reaches the end of its possible travel. This probably happens, for example, when one's finger touches a very hot object, likely to cause a serious burn. The intrafusal muscles, on the other hand, work against a well-damped elastic load with no inertia. The same control signal sent down the fusimotor nerves will make these fibres shorten by a certain distance, exciting the stretch receptors; the stretch reflex will operate and the main muscle fibres will shorten by the same distance, until the stretch reflex is no longer excited. The movement is obviously more precise and better controlled. In some circumstances, however, there may be a steady state displacement error. Suppose, for example, that the main muscles are lifting an arm or leg from the vertical position (hanging down) towards the horizontal position; there will be an opposing force, derived from the weight of the arm or leg, which varies with the position. In order to maintain some particular position, a maintained exciting signal must be sent to the muscles, the misalignment at the stretch receptors will not be reduced to zero, and the follow-up will not be exact. A suitable proportion of the control signal, applied directly to the main motor nerve fibres, apart from any signal derived from the stretch receptors, would act as an input feed forward and correct the error. Such direct excitation of the main muscles does occur; but if it is to be just sufficient to remove the steady state error, its magnitude must be related to the load on the muscles. Now it is known from observations on the action potentials in the afferent nerves coming from a muscle that there are receptors which discharge at a frequency which is more or less proportional to the *force* exerted by the muscle—unlike the stretch receptors, whose discharge frequency depends on the *length* of the muscle. These receptors lie on the tendons which connect the muscle fibres to the bones; being elastic, the tendons are stretched, when the muscle fibres contract, by an amount which depends on the tension set up in them. At present, we have no definite knowledge of the function of these tendon receptors; it may be that they are concerned in regulating the amount of input feed forward sent down the main motor nerve fibres.

The follow-up system probably comes into action after one's finger has been withdrawn from the hot object. In the simplest possible conditions, the finger would drop back on to the hot object again, since the stimulus for withdrawal has been removed: but the "adaptive", elementary learning properties of the nervous system come into play; the appropriate muscles are "biased" by means of their intrafusal muscles, and the finger is moved to some other place.

Contraction of the intrafusal muscles, also, is responsible for the bias provided by the "auxiliary" muscles which help to maintain balance when one is standing, and referred to on p. 117 above. If these are made to contract slightly, just enough to lengthen the stretch receptors up to the threshold at which they start to initiate impulses, the sensitivity to "disturbances" tending to stretch the whole muscle will be increased. The stretch reflex will be set up by a smaller deviation from the position of balance, and the amplitude of the oscillations will be reduced.

CONTROL OF ORIENTATION IN PLANTS

The direction in which the shoots and roots of a plant are growing is detected by receptor systems in the cells of the growing tips. If a growing rootlet, for example, is inclined to the vertical,

E*

starch grains within the cells at the tip fall under the influence of gravity and come to lie on the lower side of the cell, rather than on one end. By some unknown process, this results in the transmission of a "growth hormone" (or "*auxin*") preferentially to cells on the opposite (upper) side of the rootlet, a few millimetres away. These are the effectors of the system, and under the influence of the greater supply of auxin enlarge more rapidly than do the corresponding cells on the same (lower) side as the excited receptors. The rootlet thus grows in a curve until it is directed vertically downwards. The same type of control is exerted in growing shoots, except that the auxin is transmitted preferentially to the effector (enlarging) cells on the same (lower) side as the excited receptors, and the shoot curves until it is growing vertically upwards. This kind of control system operates, also, in those shoots which grow towards the light. The receptor cells are sensitive to the intensity of the illumination falling on them, which ordinarily is greater on the side facing the light: in some kinds of plant, however, refraction within the tissues focuses the light on the side remote from the direction of the illumination. Climbing plants, again, which curl round supporting posts, for example, have receptors which are sensitive to contact with external objects. In all these, the effectors are the growing (enlarging) cells a few millimetres away from the extreme tip where the cells are first formed by repeated division of each cell into two cells.

There is rather little quantitative information about the behaviour of these control systems. There is a threshold in all of them which is peculiar in being defined by a critical value of the time integral of the misalignment. If a plant is subjected to an appropriate centrifugal force, it responds in the same way as it does to a gravitational force: for a detectable response just to be produced, the product of the centrifugal (or gravitational) force and the time during which it is made to act (the "presentation time") is constant. Under a gravitational stimulus, the presentation times, in most kinds of plant, lie between one minute and a few tens of minutes. It may be that the presentation time is determined by, or at least related to, the time taken for the starch grains to fall on to the receptor surface; or, in the response to light, for some photochemical reaction to "advance" by some critical amount. After the threshold has been reached, there is a "latent period", or finite delay, before there is any detectable response by the effectors: some investigators consider that the response is then "all-or-nothing", so that the whole system is an on-off one.

This is undoubtedly an over-simplified account of the behaviour of the control systems, and detailed examination shows that there may be elaborations which differ in different kinds of plant. But from the general principles of the action of control systems, one would expect that the combination of integral control with a finite delay, even in an on-off system, would be apt to produce instability. There is no evidence, however, that this occurs under any ordinary conditions.

CONTROL OF THE BLOOD CIRCULATION IN ANIMALS

The rate of flow of blood to any particular organ, or group of cells with similar functions, is controlled primarily by a local system within the organ itself: as the metabolic rate of the constituent cells increases and decreases, the blood vessels supplying the organ are opened and closed, increasing and decreasing the blood flow accordingly. Rather little is known about the way in which these control systems operate. They could not be effective, however, unless there were arrangements by which the pressure of the blood in the main supply trunks (the large arteries) was kept more or less constant. If a substantial fraction of all the cells in the animal were to make a large increase in the demand for a flow of blood, the pressure in the main arteries would drop. In the absence of some means of compensation, it might well become impossible for the demand of the active cells to be satisfied: some of the other cells, moreover, might get less than their minimum demand, and either fail to carry out some essential function, or, through their local control systems, increase their own blood supply and so exacerbate the condition.

Control of the blood pressure

There are three main groups of receptors, or misalignment detectors, in the walls of the large arteries, which are sensitive to changes in the general, or "systemic" blood pressure (they have been referred to already in Chapter 5): all appear to behave in much the same way, and to form components of the same control system.

The magnitude of the systemic blood pressure at any moment is determined by the product of the quantity of blood that the heart pumps out in unit time and the resistance to the flow of blood through the vessels: this "peripheral resistance" depends on the diameter of the blood vessels, and is increased by contraction, decreased by relaxation, of muscle cells in their walls. These muscles, together with those responsible for the pumping action of the heart, are the "motors" in the pressure control system.

In ordinary circumstances, when an animal is at rest or moving about slowly, changes in the blood pressure, as detected by the pressure-sensitive receptors, are corrected almost entirely by adjustment of the peripheral resistance. Oddly enough, the control system works backwards, as it were. The "controller" in the nervous system is so arranged that in the absence of a control signal the peripheral resistance is kept large: when the general blood pressure is at the set point, the receptors receive a moderate excitation, and the control signal partially inhibits this inherent constrictor action on the blood vessels; if the blood pressure falls below the set point, the inhibitory control signal is reduced, the peripheral resistance rises, and the blood pressure is restored to the set point; when the blood pressure rises above the set point, the control signal is increased and the peripheral resistance falls.

Some quantitative studies have been made on this control system. From the response to step function inputs, for example, it is known that there is a finite delay of several seconds, and that there may be some overshoot in the response, so that the system may be slightly underdamped. Some measurements with simple harmonic inputs have shown that at very low frequencies (less than 0.01 cycles per second) the output is in phase with the input, phase lags appearing only at higher frequencies (for example $-90°$ at 0.04 c/s). There may be some error rate control, since part of the response of the receptors is known to be "rapidly adapting", depending on the time derivative of the excitation.

Reflex constriction of the blood vessels is over-ridden by the dilatation produced locally by any groups of cells which are not getting as much blood as they need: control of the blood pressure by control of the peripheral resistance will fail if there are too many such groups. But any considerable increase in the metabolic rate of any group of cells is accompanied by an increase in the output of the heart, whether there is any change in the blood pressure or not; this acts, therefore, as an input feed forward in the pressure control system. It is brought about in several ways.

One is an indirect result of the increased depth of breathing necessary to take in oxygen at an increased rate, as will be described in the next section: blood is drawn into the large veins in the chest at a greater rate, and the heart automatically pumps it out again at the same rate. Another, providing a different kind of input feed forward, may be illustrated by an example. When an animal runs, impulses travel down the motor nerves to the muscles concerned: at the same time, impulses are sent to the "controller" (the "vasomotor centres" in the brain) of the pressure control system. These not only block any inhibitory impulses that may come in from the pressure-sensitive receptors, but also initiate fresh impulses which travel to the heart, causing it to beat more rapidly and more forcibly; other excitatory impulses are sent to the glands which secrete the hormone adrenaline, whose actions imitate and reinforce those of the "sympathetic" nerves, augmenting the output of the heart and constricting the blood vessels to relatively inactive groups of cells. Any tendency for the local control systems in the active muscles to defeat their own ends is thus avoided. The effect, indeed, is usually more than sufficient for this, and the general blood pressure rises.

The existence of this kind of input feed forward is demonstrated by the fact that the signals may be applied to the vasomotor centres *before* the muscles are excited, in consequence, for example, of fear or the anticipation of a need for "fight or flight" (as W. B. Cannon expressed it). The demand for an increased supply of blood to the muscles does not yet exist, and the compensatory changes necessary to provide for this demand are thus very obvious. Most people are familiar with the pale cold skin (constriction of the blood vessels) and the rapid powerful throbbing pulse (increase in frequency and strength of the heart beat)— both characteristic of the action of adrenaline—when they are afraid or faced with some emergency.

Frequency response curves of a blood pressure control system. Of the organs referred to above which fail to carry out essential functions if their blood supply is inadequate, the nervous system (including the brain) is the most important. If it fails, nearly all the control systems necessary for the well-being, or even survival, of the animal fail also. To a large extent, its blood supply is maintained by means of the general pressure control system, since the arteries running to it are not constricted when the blood pressure falls. But there is also what is probably an "emergency" system: when the blood supply to the brain becomes inadequate, the inherent constrictor action of the vasomotor centres is augmented, and the peripheral resistance increased.

It is possible to open the loop of this part of the general pressure control system. The arteries supplying blood to the head of an anaesthetised dog may be tied off, leaving all the nervous connections between the head and the rest of the animal intact. The head can then be supplied with blood ("perfused") at any desired pressure from the circulation of another anaesthetised dog, this pressure being independent of any control exerted by the perfused head. When this is done, it is found that in the steady state there is an inverse relation between the pressure at which blood is supplied to the head and the general blood pressure in the dog whose head is being perfused: when the perfusion pressure is small, (well below the normal set point of the system), the blood vessels in the body of the dog are made to constrict and the peripheral resistance rises; when the perfusion pressure is raised, the peripheral resistance falls. The relation between head pressure and general blood pressure is non-linear, approximately hyperbolic: when the head perfusion pressure is large (at or above the normal set-point) a small change has little effect on the general blood pressure; when the head pressure is small, a small change has a large effect on the general pressure.

An approximate loop transfer locus may be plotted by superimposing on the steady perfusion pressure a simple harmonic fluctuation of small amplitude at any desired frequency, and measuring the amplitude and phase of the consequent fluctuations in the general blood pressure. Three such loci, at different values of the steady background pressure, are plotted in *Figure 34*. When plotting these, the output is taken to be in phase with the misalignment when the negative peak of the fluctuations in general blood pressure is synchronous with the positive peak of the fluctuations in head perfusion pressure. Owing to the arrangement of the control system, the output (as measured) would be *added* to the input at the misalignment detector if the loop were closed.

On giving the system a step function misalignment, it was found that there was a finite delay of some 10 seconds (5 to 15 seconds in different animals). Analysis of the amplitude and phase relations at different frequencies indicated that in addition there was a single exponential delay with a time constant of about

20 seconds (8 to 50 seconds in different animals) in some experiments, and two such delays in other experiments. It is likely that the muscles in the walls of the blood vessels are opposed by a visco-elastic load; this would account for one of the exponential

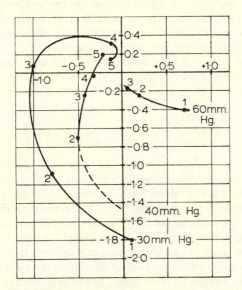

FIGURE 34 *Loop Transfer Loci (Nyqvist diagrams) for the control system which regulates the supply of blood to the brain in a dog, as described in the text.*

The three loci give the output/input amplitude and phase relations, under open loop conditions, when a small simple harmonic input pressure (amplitude between 5 and 10 mm.Hg) was superimposed on a steady pressure of 60 mm.Hg, 40 mm.Hg and 30 mm.Hg, respectively.

The frequencies corresponding to the numbered points were: (1) 1/126; (2) 1/79; (3) 1/49; (4) 1/30; (5) 1/20 (in cycles per second).

delays. The finite delay is much larger than any that could be introduced by the nervous system; its size suggests the presence of a link involving a hormone carried by the blood stream, but there is no definite evidence for this.

It is obvious from the three loci plotted in *Figure 34* that the phase lag, as well as the output/misalignment amplitude ratio, increases as the steady background perfusion pressure is made smaller. When this was as small as 30 mm.Hg, the locus passes just outside the point $(-1, 0)$; according to the Nyqvist criterion the system should be unstable in these conditions if the loop were closed. By means of a rather elaborate experimental arrangement, the fluctuations superimposed on the perfusion pressure supplying the head could be made to imitate exactly the fluctuations in the general blood pressure created by the control system: the loop is effectively closed, although the mean perfusion pressure may be set at any desired value. When this was done, and the mean perfusion pressure was small, the system did, in fact, go into permanent oscillation at about the expected frequency of 1 cycle per minute.

CONTROL OF BREATHING

The power needed to operate the chemical factories in living cells is obtained from chemical reactions between oxygen and certain substances obtained from the food, chiefly sugars; the end products of the reactions being water and carbon dioxide. In this respect, living cells do not differ from steam or petrol engines— the fuels vary, but oxygen is always needed for their combustion, and the end products are the same. Land animals take in the oxygen from the air, and expel carbon dioxide to the air, by means of their lungs. (Insects have no lungs, but take in oxygen and expel carbon dioxide, through small tubes distributed throughout their bodies and opening to the air: we will not consider this kind of breathing.) The rhythmic ventilation of the lungs absorbs power, and is regulated by a control system in such a way that the rate of intake of oxygen is equal to the rate at which the cells throughout the animal are consuming it; and that the rate of discharge of carbon dioxide is equal to the rate at which the cells are producing it. This control system is thus rather a peculiar one: the "motor" consists of the various muscles which rhythmically expand the chest, drawing air into the lungs, and allow it to collapse, expelling the air again, and its activities are, or may be, controlled by two misalignments—the quantity of oxygen and the quantity of carbon dioxide in the animal at any moment.

It is not possible to measure these misalignments directly in a living animal, but their magnitudes can be calculated from certain other quantities which can be measured. When any kind of watery solution is in contact with a mixture of different gases, the concentration of each gas in the solution, when equilibrium has been reached, becomes proportional to its "partial pressure" in the gas mixture—that is the percentage of that gas in the mixture multiplied by the total pressure of the mixture; in the lungs, this is the prevailing atmospheric pressure. Partial pressures may be expressed as percentages of the "standard" atmospheric pressure, in millibars or in millimetres of mercury. (The standard atmospheric pressure is 1000 mb or 760 mm.Hg.) The constant of proportionality is the "solubility" of the particular gas considered in the watery solution concerned; this can be measured in the laboratory. Now the composition of the various solutions within an animal—the blood, the extracellular fluid surrounding the cells, and the intracellular fluid within them—does not vary very much from one individual to another, and is reasonably well known; the solubility of oxygen and carbon dioxide in these solutions is also known. The total volume of each of these solutions, moreover, can be measured, even in a living animal. Thus the total quantities of oxygen and carbon dioxide in the animal can be calculated from measurements of the partial pressures of these gases with which the solutions are in equilibrium. The solubilities are sensibly constant, at least over periods of a few hours, and it is conventional to measure the misalignment in the control system in terms of the partial pressures only.

The blood leaving the lungs is, for most practical purposes, in equilibrium with the air with which it has been in contact— the so-called "alveolar air": samples of this can be obtained without difficulty and its composition measured. (This is substantially different from that of the outside air.) It is convenient, therefore, as a first approximation, to use the partial pressures of oxygen and carbon dioxide in the alveolar air as measures of the misalignment in the system which controls breathing. This must, of course, be incorrect, and the error will vary in different circumstances. In the blood entering the lungs, the partial pressure of oxygen must be less than that of the alveolar air and the partial pressure of carbon dioxide greater, otherwise there would be no transfer of these gases into or out of the blood; in the rest of the animal, the partial pressures will, on the average, have some intermediate values.

The use of the partial pressures as measures of the misalignment, moreover, introduces certain complications into the analysis of the behaviour of the control system. The solubility of oxygen in

E**

all the body fluids except the blood is small, so that practically all the oxygen in the animal at any moment is in the blood. Here it is in chemical combination with the substance haemoglobin which gives the blood its red colour, and the relation between the concentration of oxygen and the partial pressure of oxygen is extremely non-linear. In the arterial blood coming from the lungs, the haemoglobin is very nearly saturated with oxygen, and the oxygen concentration is virtually independent of the partial pressure: the blood in the veins coming back to the lungs has lost oxygen to the cells which are consuming it, the oxygen concentration is about one-half to two-thirds of the saturation value and changes rapidly with changes in the partial pressure.

Carbon dioxide combines with constituents of all the body fluids. In watery solution it forms an acid, carbonic acid, and this reacts chemically with the salts (chiefly sodium and potassium salts) of other acids, (chiefly proteins and phosphates), forming bicarbonates. The reactions may be represented concisely as:

$$CO_2 + H_2O \rightleftharpoons H_2CO_3$$

$$H_2CO_3 + A^- + Na^+ \rightleftharpoons HCO_3^- + Na^+ + HA$$

where HA represents the acidic protein or phosphate. The reactions are reversible, and the equilibrium condition moves to the right or the left according to the concentration (partial pressure) of carbon dioxide in the solution. The relation between the total quantity of carbon dioxide in the animal and the partial pressure in the alveolar air is non-linear, but less so than that between the quantity of oxygen and the partial pressure of oxygen, and there is no saturation. More important than the non-linearity, however, is the fact that these reactions occur in all the body fluids. Suppose that the activity, and metabolic rate, of a certain group of cells suddenly increases: the rate of production of carbon dioxide, and hence the partial pressure of carbon dioxide in the blood leaving the group of cells, will also increase suddenly. But as the blood flows round the rest of the animal, carbon dioxide will diffuse out and react with the weak acids in the whole body fluids; the average partial pressure of carbon dioxide in the whole animal will thus reach a steady state value only gradually.

There are two sets of *misalignment detectors*. One set is in the walls of arteries in the neck, in contact with the arterial blood coming away from the lungs; they respond both to a reduction in the partial pressure of oxygen in the blood and to an increase in the partial pressure of carbon dioxide. These pressures depend on the rate at which oxygen is taken in by the lungs and carbon dioxide is expelled (the output velocity of the system) as well as on the oxygen and carbon dioxide partial pressures in the venous blood coming to the lungs (approximating to the misalignment in the system). If the misalignment is constant, an increase in the rate of ventilation of the lungs will increase the oxygen partial pressure in the blood and reduce the carbon dioxide partial pressure. These "peripheral" receptors, therefore, will deliver control signals which combine, probably in a non-linear manner, the misalignment with a negative output velocity feedback.

The other set of misalignment detectors is situated in the nervous system (in that part of the brain-stem known as the medulla) close to the structures (the "respiratory centres") which act as the "controller" of the whole system. These receptors are sensitive to an increase in the partial pressure of carbon dioxide in the solution surrounding them, but not to a decrease in the partial pressure of oxygen—they may even be put out of action if there is a considerable shortage of oxygen. These "central" receptors are not even approximately in contact with the arterial blood, and carbon dioxide reaches them by diffusion through intervening fluids where it reacts chemically and is partly absorbed, as already discussed. The conditions, therefore, are just those discussed in Chapter 3 which give rise to an *exponential delay*, simple or possibly distributed, at the receptors.

There will also be *finite delays*. In man, it takes some 5 to 15 seconds for a change in the carbon dioxide content of the blood, consequent on a change in the metabolic rate of some group of cells, to reach the central receptors in the brain: the changes in the carbon dioxide and oxygen content will reach the peripheral receptors after a somewhat shorter delay, since the blood has not quite so far to travel. Further, breathing is a rhythmic process and ordinarily air is drawn in actively, and blown out passively by the elastic recoil of the lungs: any sudden change in the control signal cannot take effect on the motor until the beginning of the next active expansion of the chest—i.e. after a delay which will vary from zero to about 30 seconds in man, according to the frequency of the breathing and the phase at which the change occurs.

Effects of changing the output load

Ordinarily, breathing is controlled by the carbon dioxide misalignment. This was first shown conclusively by experiments carried out in Oxford by J. S. Haldane and J. G. Priestley in 1905; these have become "classical" in the development of our knowledge of the physiology of breathing. They consisted in making a human subject breathe air containing varying percentages of carbon dioxide (ordinary air contains only 0.03 per cent) and measuring the changes in the volume of air which he breathed in and out in unit time (sometimes known as the "ventilation rate") and the changes in the percentage of carbon dioxide in the alveolar air. Now if Q is the volume of air taken into, and expelled from, the lungs by each breath (corrected for any departure of the barometric pressure from the standard value), f is the frequency of breathing, p_e is the percentage of carbon dioxide in the air expelled and p_i is the percentage in the air taken in, the quantity of carbon dioxide removed from the lungs in unit time is $Q f (p_e - p_i)$. This is the output of the motor. The input to the system (the rate of production of carbon dioxide) is unchanged in these experiments, and if the output is also to remain unchanged in spite of, say, an increase in the value of p_i either p_e must increase equally, or the product $Q f$ must increase. Now p_e is related to p_a, the percentage of carbon dioxide in the alveolar air, but is not identical with it: some of the air taken in on each breath fails to reach the alveoli of the lungs, where it comes into contact with the blood, but remains in the "dead space". Nevertheless, if p_e increases, so also will p_a, and thus the carbon dioxide misalignment of the animal. If this is an important component of the control system, there will be an increase in the rate of working of the "motor" and an increase in $Q f$; alternatively, (assuming there is no integral control) there can be no increase in $Q f$ without an increase in p_a and p_e. This, in fact, is what is observed. In effect, by increasing p_i we are increasing the load on the motor—it has to work harder in order to produce the same output rate—and we may expect a corresponding increase in the steady state velocity error.

If the control system behaves in a linear manner there will be an approximately linear relation between the percentage of carbon dioxide in the alveolar air and the ventilation rate. This has been observed experimentally, as is shown in *Figure 35*, which epresents the results of some more extensive experiments than

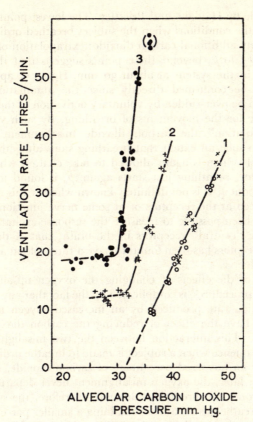

FIGURE 35   *Control of breathing in man.*

A human subject was made to breathe air containing varying percentages of carbon dioxide and oxygen. His ventilation rate (volume of air breathed in and out of the lungs in each minute) is plotted against the partial pressure of carbon dioxide in the alveolar air (in mm.Hg).

The plotted points lie on three different lines according to the partial pressure of oxygen in the alveolar air.

　　Line 1: 110 mm Hg (o) and approximately 170 mm.Hg (×);
　　Line 2: approximately 47 mm.Hg (+);
　　Line 3: approximately 37 mm.Hg (●).

If the carbon dioxide pressure is less than about 30 mm.Hg, breathing is controlled only by the oxygen pressure.

(From Nielsen and Smith. *Acta physiologica Scandinavica*, vol. 24, *Figure 4*, p. 298 (1951)).

those made by Haldane and Priestley. The lowest points plotted
represent the conditions when the subject breathed ordinary air,
without any additional carbon dioxide: extrapolation of the line
relating Qf to p_a beyond these points suggests that there is a
threshold in the system at about 30 mm. Hg (p = approx. 4).
This can be confirmed directly since the automatic control
system can be over-ridden by voluntary activation of the muscles
responsible for the movements of breathing. By such voluntary
"over-ventilation" the carbon dioxide misalignment can be
reduced to such an extent that breathing stops altogether when
the control system is again allowed to take charge; when, after
a short time, breathing just starts again, p_a is found to have a
value of about 4. It is not definitely known whether this threshold
is introduced at the receptors or at some nerve junctions. It has
not so far been possible to measure the response/excitation relation of the "central" receptors in the brain; that of the "peripheral" receptors has been found to have a threshold at about the
correct value.

Studies of the effects of changing the oxygen misalignment,
by similar procedures, is complicated by the fact that any increase
in ventilation rate produced by an increased oxygen misalignment will have the effect of reducing the carbon dioxide misalignment. (This interaction between the two misalignments is
of no consequence when a subject is made to breathe ordinary air
containing an increased percentage of carbon dioxide, since, as
will appear later, the oxygen misalignment never departs signifi-
cantly beyond the threshold value.) If, therefore, the subject is
made to breathe gas mixtures containing a smaller percentage of
oxygen than has ordinary air, it is essential to increase the
percentage of carbon dioxide at the same time to such a value that
the carbon dioxide misalignment (measured as the percentage
of carbon dioxide in the alveolar air) is not changed. This can
only be done by trial and error. No extensive series of measurements of the relation between the ventilation rate and the
percentage of oxygen in the alveolar air has been made: but the
general nature of the relation can be seen from the family of
curves plotted in *Figure 35*.

In these experiments the gas mixtures breathed by the subject
were adjusted so that the relation between ventilation rate and
alveolar carbon dioxide percentage could be plotted at a number
of different, and sensibly constant, values of the alveolar oxygen

percentage. The measurements show, *first*, that an increase in alveolar oxygen percentage above about 14.5 (partial pressure 110 mm.Hg) had no effect on the ventilation rate. (This is the value observed when the subject was breathing ordinary air.) Study of the frequency of nerve impulses initiated by the oxygen-sensitive receptors has shown that there is a threshold at about the same value of the partial pressure of oxygen. *Second*, when the conditions were such that the carbon dioxide misalignment was below the threshold value, breathing continued if the oxygen misalignment was above its threshold value (i.e. the partial pressure of oxygen in the alveoli was less than 110 mm.Hg). From the two values at which measurements were made, it appears that the relation between the ventilation rate and the departure of the oxygen partial pressure from the threshold is non-linear, the stiffness increasing rapidly with increase in the apparent misalignment. But, as already remarked, the true misalignment is the oxygen content of the subject; owing to the nature of the equilibrium conditions between haemoglobin and oxygen, there is a very non-linear relation between oxygen content and reduction of oxygen partial pressure below the threshold value. The ventilation rate may thus have a more nearly linear relation with the true misalignment. The frequency of nerve impulses from the oxygen receptors, however, has been found to increase linearly with reduction in the partial pressure of oxygen in the solution surrounding them. If the results of these two sets of observations are indeed correct, then it would appear that a non-linearity of the appropriate kind is introduced by the "controller" (the respiratory centres) in the nervous system. *Third*, the slope of the line relating ventilation rate to carbon dioxide partial pressure increases as the oxygen partial pressure is reduced below the threshold. It appears, therefore, that the oxygen misalignment is not simply added to the carbon dioxide misalignment in the respiratory centres, but that each is to some extent multiplied by the other. The sensitivity (response/excitation ratio) of the oxygen receptors has, in fact, been found to be increased by increase in the carbon dioxide pressure.

Transient responses. Immediately after a man (or an anaesthetised dog) is suddenly made to breathe a gas mixture containing an increased percentage of carbon dioxide (say between 4 per cent and 7 per cent) both the arterial carbon dioxide pressure and the ventilation rate rise more or less exponentially with time, the former more rapidly (time constant about 1 minute) than the latter (time constant about 4 minutes). The carbon dioxide partial pressure in the fluid which is probably in contact with the central receptors rises more slowly than that in the arterial blood in contact with the peripheral receptors, as might be expected from its more remote position, as discussed on p. 133 above. The time course of the change (as measured in a dog) agrees reasonably well with a curve plotted on the assumption that in addition to the exponential delay (time constant 1 min.) at the peripheral receptors, there is a finite delay of some 5 to 10 secs., while the blood is flowing to the brain, and an additional exponential delay, with a time constant of about 5 mins., while the carbon dioxide is diffusing to the receptors. Thus the ventilation rate increases more rapidly than does the misalignment signal applied to the central receptors: detailed study of its time course suggests that the "motor" is activated by a control signal which is an additive combination of the signals from the two sets of receptors, in about equal proportions, together, perhaps, with a small amount of derivative signal from the peripheral receptors. The system is clearly at least critically damped, and possibly somewhat over-damped, in spite of the fact that initially, at least, the output velocity feedback to the peripheral receptors is absent, or may even be positive instead of negative. (The percentage of carbon dioxide in the inspired air is initially greater than that in the alveolar air.) The increased load on the "motor", however, will provide additional damping to compensate for this.

When the animal (or man) is allowed to breathe ordinary air again, the ventilation rate returns to the normal value more rapidly than it rose when the carbon dioxide mixture was first breathed: this is to be expected, since the load on the motor is smaller. The time course of the transient response of the system, in both conditions, is definitely not strictly exponential: detailed analysis, however, is complicated by the fact that during this period the carbon dioxide pressure in the alveoli, and in the expired air, is rising (or falling) progressively. Both the load on the motor and the output velocity feedback are varying with time and the system is thus non-linear.

The transient response to a sudden decrease in the percentage of oxygen in the inspired air (say to about 10 per cent instead of the normal 21 per cent) indicates that the system is then very under-damped and may actually become unstable. The response varies quite considerably in different individuals; but usually the breathing becomes *periodic*, as shown in *Figure 36*: the depth of breathing (the volume taken in on each breath) rises and falls rhythmically, and in severe conditions breathing may stop altogether at regular intervals. When this happens, both misalignments (as measured by the fall in partial pressure of oxygen, and rise in that of carbon dioxide, in the alveolar air) alternately fall below their thresholds and rise above them. In most circumstances, the system settles down, after a few cycles, to a steady state. This is just how an under-damped system, with threshold, would be expected to behave, as is brought out in the theoretical discussion in Chapter 6 (p. 104). It is not certain whether the reduction in effective damping is due only to the increase in the stiffness of the system, or whether there may also be some increase in the time constants of the delays. There can be little doubt, however, that when the system is operating on both the carbon dioxide misalignment and the oxygen misalignment, the stiffness is considerably greater than it is when operating on either alone.

Figure 36 (a) is a record of the movements of J. S. Haldane's chest when he breathed a gas mixture containing 10.64 per cent of oxygen (about one-half that in ordinary air). The increased rate of ventilation consequent on the rather sudden increase in the oxygen misalignment (decrease in oxygen content of the body fluids) would be expected to lower the carbon dioxide content relatively slowly, owing to the diffusion delays already mentioned: it probably remained above the threshold value during the first two minutes, while the breathing was periodic, and then fell permanently below the threshold, with a corresponding decrease in stiffness, and increase in damping, so that a more or less steady state was reached. Transient, very marked, periodic breathing occurred again when he returned to breathing ordinary air. The oxygen misalignment fell rapidly to below the threshold, but at first the carbon dioxide misalignment was also below the threshold and breathing stopped: both misalignments then steadily increased until breathing started; but the damping was sufficiently small (the stiffness sufficiently large) for the control system to overshoot and reduce both misalignments to below their thresholds again. After three cycles, however, the control system settled down (the non-linearity in the response to a reduction in the oxygen content being useful here), the oxygen misalignment remaining permanently below its threshold and the carbon dioxide misalignment permanently above its threshold. A very similar transient period of instability of the control system usually

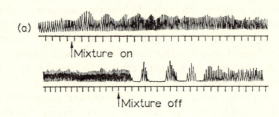

(a)

Mixture on

Mixture off

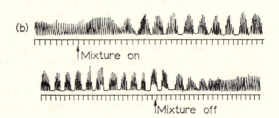

(b)

Mixture on

Mixture off

FIGURE 36   *The movements of breathing when the air contains little oxygen, showing "periodic breathing".*

The height of the record is a rough measure of the volume of air taken in on each breath.

(a) The air breathed contained 10·64 per cent oxygen: there were transient oscillations, of small amplitude, initially; and transient, very marked oscillations when ordinary air was breathed again. The system was reasonably stable in the steady state.

(b) The air breathed contained 11·05 per cent oxygen and 0·7 per cent carbon dioxide: the system became unstable and oscillation, giving periodic breathing, was maintained.

Below the records are time marks in 10 second intervals. The two parts of each record are continuous.

(From J. S. Haldane and J. G. Priestley, "Respiration", *Figure 57*, p. 196. Oxford: at the Clarendon Press, 1935.)

occurs after voluntary over-breathing, sufficient to stop automatic breathing for a time, as described on p. 136 above.

Figure 36 (b) shows the movements of Haldane's chest when he breathed a gas mixture containing 11·05 per cent oxygen and 0·7 per cent carbon dioxide. The additional carbon dioxide prevented the carbon dioxide misalignment from falling permanently below its threshold; the control system remained permanently unstable, a limit cycle was reached, and periodic breathing continued indefinitely. Such permanent instability may occur in some people when they breathe air containing an appropriate, not too small, percentage of oxygen without any additional carbon dioxide: J. G. Priestley, for example, developed a maintained periodic breathing on 10·33 per cent oxygen, but not on 9·59 per cent oxygen. It is apt to occur, also, at high altitudes (above 10,000 feet), owing to the low barometric pressure and consequent low partial pressure of oxygen in the alveoli: it can be very inconvenient and even distressing, since it is particularly likely to occur when one is lying down and trying to sleep. A supply of oxygen is useful for preventing this.

Effects of changing the input rate

These studies on the behaviour of the system controlling breathing have been made by using rather artificial kinds of disturbance. A more natural method is to make a sudden change in the rate of input to the system and to study the subsequent changes in the rate of output and in the misalignment. The only way in which the rate of consumption of oxygen and the rate of production of carbon dioxide can be suddenly and substantially increased is by making the animal, or man, take muscular exercise. When this is done, the behaviour of the system is found to be quite different from that just described. By taking exercise, the ventilation rate can be increased to a value considerably greater than that produced by breathing gas mixtures containing an excess of carbon dioxide, but the partial pressure of carbon dioxide in the alveolar air, and in the arterial blood, increases by a much smaller amount, and the increase may be too small to detect.

There are two reasons why the increase in the carbon dioxide misalignment, for any given increase in ventilation rate, may be smaller in exercise than it is when the inspired air contains excess carbon dioxide. *First*, there may be some increase in the oxygen misalignment (reduction in the partial pressure of oxygen in the arterial blood), although this is always small and usually negligible. *Secondly*, if the exercise is severe (not far from the limit set by the capabilities of the animal or man) lactic acid may be released by the muscles. In order to avoid unnecessary confusion, we have so far assumed that the misalignment receptors respond only to the partial pressure of carbon dioxide in the fluids surrounding them. In point of fact, the exciting stimulus is the *acidity* of these fluids: in the presence of some other acid, such as lactic acid, they will generate an increased misalignment signal even though there is no increase in the partial pressure of carbon dioxide. The results of a great deal of experimental study, however, have shown that these two factors cannot by themselves account for the observed disproportion between the increase in ventilation rate and the increase in alveolar carbon dioxide pressure: the breathing is not controlled solely by the carbon dioxide misalignment.

An important additional factor is the existence of input feed forward: signals, more or less proportional to the rate at which the muscles are working, are sent to the respiratory centres, and the ventilation rate is increased whether or not there is any "drive" from the carbon dioxide and oxygen misalignments. Part of the signal which reaches the active muscles in the form of impulses in their motor nerves, is sent, also, to the respiratory centres (just as it is sent to the vasomotor centres, as already described). Unless the animal, or man, has prior knowledge of the kind and severity of the exercise to be taken, the magnitude of this signal may be quite inappropriate. For example, if a man is told that he is about to work hard against a large load, and is then given only a small load, the ventilation rate will at first be much too large, and it will settle down to the appropriate steady value after a series of oscillations: during these, the alveolar carbon dioxide pressure falls and rises inversely with the ventilation rate. More important, possibly, than the signals derived from the motor nerves are signals derived from receptors in the working muscles: the "stretch receptors" in the muscles, and receptors in the joints between the bones, will initiate signals whose magnitude is at least partly and approximately proportional to the rate of movement of the muscles; the receptors in the tendons, between the muscle fibres and the bones which they move, will initiate signals depending on the force exerted by the muscles. The product of the signals from the movement receptors and the force (or tension) receptors will thus give an input feed forward which depends on the rate of working of the muscles, and thus on the increase in the rate of oxygen consumption and the rate of carbon dioxide production, or the increase in the rate of input to the control system.

It is not generally agreed, however, that the whole control of breathing during muscular exercise is brought about by the carbon dioxide misalignment, together with the lactic acid production (if any), the oxygen misalignment (if any) and the input feed forward from the working muscles. Some investigators think that there must be some other factors which have not yet been identified.

CONTROL OF SIZE AND SHAPE

By the size and shape of an animal or plant, we ordinarily mean its general external appearance, determined by the nature and relative proportions of its various parts. These parts—not only those visible from the outside, but also the internal organs—have their own characteristic sizes and shapes, and each consists of an assembly of cells characteristic of that part or organ. (Some of the "parts" into which the whole animal or plant is divided on superficial observation may contain assemblies of several different kinds of cell; legs, for example, contain both bones and muscles.) Microscopic observation shows that different kinds of cell have different sizes and shapes, particularly in respect of their internal structures or "organelles": by electron microscopy we can see, approximately, the sizes and shapes of the larger "macromolecules" within the cells. Smaller molecules are characterised by studying their chemical properties; this is an indirect way of observing their sizes and shapes.

Growth and differentiation

Every animal and plant begins as an egg-cell, derived from the female parent, which has been "fertilised" by a sperm cell, derived from the male parent: the fertilised egg, therefore, must contain all the "information" and "templates" necessary for the subsequent production of all the molecules, cells, and organs, with their characteristic sizes and shapes. The egg cell develops into the animal or plant by a process of division, first into two cells, then into 4, into 8, and so on, eventually reaching billions. (There are about 10^{10} cells in the human brain, for example.) Between divisions, the cells enlarge, fresh material of the appropriate kind being synthesised out of relatively simple substances present in the solution outside the cells. As the number of cells increases, different groups of cells become "differentiated" from one another, synthesising different kinds of material and taking up the special compositions and shapes appropriate to the various organs and parts of the whole animal or plant.

Study of the way in which recognisable "characters" (sizes and shapes) are inherited from one generation to the next, showed that the "information" about these characters resides in structural units called "genes". (These studies were begun by Mendel, abbot of Brünn, now Brno in Czechoslovakia, who published in 1866.) These genes are ordinarily invisible: but shortly before a cell starts the rather elaborate process of division, its genes join up into a number of threads, called "chromosomes", which can be seen, after suitable treatment, under the microscope. In the course of division, each chromosome splits longitudinally into two parts, one part going into each of the "daughter" cells: each of these cells, therefore, contains the same number of chromosomes as the parent cell and a complete set of genes. Every cell into which the egg divides should, therefore, be capable of developing into a complete animal or plant of the proper kind: and this is so, up to the stage at which the cells begin to become differentiated. The activities of some of the genes, presumably, then become depressed, and that of others enhanced, or perhaps modified. How this occurs is unknown, although there are some suggestive possibilities.

Control of chemical reactions in living cells

We must first digress a little. Most of the chemical reactions that occur in living cells cannot be made to "go" in a test-tube, at least at anything like the speed that they go in living cells; this applies particularly to the reactions by which the constituents of the cells are built up from the substances supplied from the environment. The reason for this is that living cells possess "enzymes" which are catalysts and increase the speed of the chemical reactions within the cell. (Many of these can be extracted from the cells and their catalytic properties studied in the laboratory.) Enzymes have two important properties. (1) They are extremely powerful as catalysts, so much so that the reactions within a cell are, for all practical purposes, brought about by the presence of the appropriate enzymes. (Strictly, the reactions must go in the absence of the enzymes, but the rate may be quite indetectable.) (2) They are very specific, in the sense that an enzyme which "makes" two substances react in a certain way has little or no effect in making two very similar substances react in the same, or any other, way: if these two other substances do react, then they are made to do so by a different enzyme. The particular kinds of reaction which occur in any particular cell, therefore—i.e. the nature of its differentiation—will be decided by the particular kinds of enzyme which it contains, and which it, or its parent cells, must have made.

Enzymes consist of two parts: a "prosthetic" group or "co-enzyme", which may, for example, be a metal atom such as iron or copper in organic combination, or a relatively simple organic compound; and a large protein molecule or "apo-enzyme" to which the prosthetic group, or co-enzyme, is attached. The general nature of the reaction catalysed—e.g. "oxidation" by the transfer of an electron or hydrogen atom to, say, molecular oxygen, or synthesis, by joining together two molecules with the removal of a molecule of water—is decided by the nature of the prosthetic group or co-enzyme. The specificity, the particular kinds of molecule which are made to react, is decided by the nature of the protein apo-enzyme. We can thus take a step further and conclude that the detailed nature of the chemical reactions carried out by any particular cell will be decided by the particular kinds of protein which it is able to synthesise: and this takes us back to the "templates" in the genes.

All proteins consist of long chains of amino-acids: all amino-acids are chemically very similar, with the same basic "structural formula":

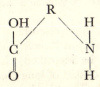

They differ from one another, and are identified, by the particular atom, or collection of atoms forming an organic group, which is represented by the letter R: in the simplest amino-acid, R is a hydrogen atom; in the more complicated ones, R is a ring structure of carbon, or carbon and nitrogen, atoms. A molecule of a protein is formed by joining together, end to end, hundreds, thousands or tens of thousands of amino-acid molecules, a molecule of water being removed at each junction:

$$R_1 \quad\quad O \quad\quad H \quad\quad R_3$$
$$| \quad\quad\quad || \quad\quad\quad | \quad\quad\quad |$$
$$C \quad\quad\quad C \quad\quad\quad N \quad\quad\quad C$$

OH $/$ $|$ $\backslash$ $\quad/$ $\quad\backslash$ $\quad/$ $\quad\backslash$ $\quad/$ $\quad\backslash$ etc.

$$| \quad H \quad\quad N \quad\quad\quad C \quad\quad\quad C \quad\quad\quad N$$
$$C$$
$$||$$
$$O \quad\quad\quad\quad\quad R_2 \quad\quad\quad O \quad\quad\quad H$$

(R_1, R_2 and R_3 represent different groups or "side-chains".)
The direction in which the bonds stick out from the carbon and
nitrogen atoms makes the whole chain take up a cork-screw,
or helical, shape with the side-chains sticking out sideways:
this is represented on paper by a zig-zag, with every alternate
amino-acid upside down. In living cells, there are only 20 different
amino-acids, but an enormous, and unknown, number of different
proteins: the nature of the protein, therefore, must be determined
almost entirely by the *order* in which the various amino-acids are
put together. This order is decided by the "template".

Nature of the "templates". There is one complication which must
be dealt with before going any further. The genes are contained
within an inner compartment of the cell known as the "nucleus".
The chemical reactions by which the various substances necessary
for the enlargement and differentiation of the cell occur in the
remainder of the cell, the "cytoplasm". The genes, accordingly,
contain what might be called the "master" templates, from which
"working" templates are constructed and transmitted to the
cytoplasm.

Both kinds of template have essentially the same general kind
of structure and are known as "nucleic acids" (the ones in the
nuclei were the first to be identified). Like proteins, they are
"macro-molecules" and consist of long chains of similar, but not
quite identical, molecules. The "back-bone" of the chain consists
of a series of sugar molecules (unlike the more commonly known
sugar, glucose, they have 5 carbon atoms in each molecule
instead of 6) joined together by phosphate groups. In the "master"
templates the sugar molecules of the backbone are described by
organic chemists as de-oxyribose, the whole molecule being de-
oxyribonucleic acid, usually contracted to DNA; whereas in the
"working" templates the sugar molecules are described as ribose,
the whole molecule being ribonucleic acid, contracted to RNA.

As in the proteins, again, the backbones are helical, like cork-screws; in DNA two of these helical chains are twisted together. Attached to each sugar molecule of the backbone, both of DNA and RNA, and making one link in the chain different from another, is a rather complicated organic molecule, belonging to one of two groups of organic substances known as purines and pyrimidines. On each template there are only four different kinds: DNA has adenine, guanine, cytosine and thymine; RNA has adenine, guanine, cytosine and uracil.

The links in the DNA and RNA chain thus consist of sugar —phosphate—purine (or pyrimidine) complexes known as "nucleotides"; it is the order in which these nucleotides are arranged that characterises the template. But the arrangement of only four different kinds of nucleotide unit in the DNA and RNA chains must determine the arrangement of the 20 different kinds of amino-acid in the protein chains which are assembled on them: it is thought, therefore, that the "code" for each amino-acid is a group of three units on the DNA (or RNA) chain—e.g. ad. gu. cy., or gu. ad. cy., or gu. cy. th., or ad. cy. ur. etc.

Servo control of cellular differentiation. We may now go on to discuss how the properties of the working templates in the cytoplasm are modified during differentiation of the cell. In the first place, a fertilised egg is not homogeneous, and has axes of symmetry which are determined during its formation and "maturation". Many kinds of egg contain "yolk"—a source of nutrient materials during subsequent development—which occupies part of the cell only and produces very obvious asymmetry. (The most familiar kinds of egg, those of birds, consist almost entirely of yolk.) But even when the egg cell looks spherical and homogeneous under the microscope, it can be shown to contain long-chain molecules which are orientated, with respect to the axes of symmetry, in different directions in different parts. Thus when the cell divides, although the nuclei of the daughter cells will be identical, the cytoplasms will probably be different: these differences may affect the working templates, and possibly also, the master templates indirectly. The whole process is very complicated—much more so than the simplified account given here might suggest—and much of it is still very obscure. It would be beyond the scope of this book to go into this aspect of the problem any further, since there is another aspect in which control systems are involved.

When the protein assembled on a working template forms part of an enzyme, a "motor" is set into action, in the sense that the quantity of enzyme formed determines the *rate* at which certain chemical reactions go on—the rate, for example, at which certain constituents of the cell are synthesised. If the *quantity* of these constituents is to reach, and be held at, some set point (as in fact occurs) there must be some feedback arrangement which stops the "motor" when the set point has been reached. Experimental investigations have shown that such a feedback does exist. The investigations have been made chiefly on micro-organisms—bacteria and yeasts, for example—since they will live and grow when supplied with quite simple nutrient materials, e.g. glucose, ammonium salts, with a few other salts in low concentration, and water and oxygen: but similar results have also been obtained when cells of the "higher" animals are used, and there is no reason to suppose that the conclusions do not apply quite generally. The internal composition of these micro-organisms is not essentially different from that of any other kind of cell. They contain, for example, proteins and nucleic acids, so that they must possess enzyme systems which are capable of synthesising all the necessary amino-acids and nucleotides from the glucose and ammonium salts presented to them. But if, say, some particular amino-acid is added to the medium in which they are growing, so that they do not need to synthesise it, they stop doing so.

It has been found that there are two ways in which this negative feedback is accomplished. First, there is "end-product inhibition". The synthesis of the amino-acid (to continue with this example) takes place by a series of chemical reactions which form a sequence, or chain, the product of one reaction being the raw material of the next. When the concentration of the final product of the whole sequence reaches a certain value, the catalytic activity of one of the enzymes operating the chain is blocked—not, as a rule, that of the enzyme concerned in the formation of the final product itself, but one earlier in the sequence. The substance whose reaction is catalysed by the enzyme inhibited is usually quite different chemically from the inhibitor (the final product of the sequence); this raises biochemical difficulties as to how the block is produced.

Second, there is "repression". The accumulation of the final product in the cell blocks the working template responsible for the production of one of the enzymes necessary for its synthesis: it has been suggested that the enzyme protein molecule is no longer able to become detached from the RNA template. During the subsequent growth and division of the cell, any enzyme remaining becomes progressively diluted. Repression is clearly a more "efficient" type of feedback than is end-product inhibition, since the activities of the cell are not wasted in producing useless enzymes. But it is slower in its action, since the cell may have to divide quite a large number of times before the enzyme molecules already synthesised have disappeared. We have, however, little or no evidence as to the time relations of the processes, or, indeed, much quantitative knowledge of any kind.

In some circumstances there may be a process somewhat analogous to input feed forward. A suitable kind of micro-organism is grown in a medium of known composition, and is then transferred to another medium which contains some substance not previously present. This new substance may be utilised immediately, and presumably the necessary enzymes were already present, though not used. On the other hand, there may be an "induction" period of several hours before the new substance begins to be utilised; presumably the new enzymes are being produced during this period, in response to the presence of the new substance.

It must be admitted that the precise relevance of enzyme repression, induction and end-product inhibition to the problem of cellular differentiation is by no means obvious. One has to suppose that there are other influences at work determining the "sensitivity" of a particular cell to repression or induction, for example: there must be a very considerable "amplification" of the original asymmetry of the fertilised egg. Many suggestions have been made as to how this may occur, but nothing much is really known.

Control of the parts by the whole

Eventually, the processes of cell division and differentiation result in the production of a complete animal or plant. It is usually small at first, and lacking some of its parts (functional reproductive organs, for example): as it grows, its various parts are somehow constrained to grow at various rates such that they remain at, or take on, an appropriate size in relation to that of the whole animal or plant; it has a characteristic shape. This regulation is brought about by hormones secreted by certain cells in controlling "centres". In mammals, for example, the chief "centre" is in the anterior pituitary body, attached to the base of the brain, though not part of it. If the rate of secretion of the "growth hormone" is unduly small, the animal becomes a dwarf; if it is excessively large, the animal becomes a giant. In addition, there are other specific hormones which control the rate of growth of certain parts of the animal only. Secretion of some of these is controlled by "trophic" hormones secreted by the anterior pituitary body, and is self-regulating: an increase in the concentration of the specific hormone suppresses the secretion of the trophic hormone and so stops its own secretion. There must, presumably, be some feedback from the "target organs" on which the specific hormones act, determined by their size: how this works is not known. A less complicated example of the control of shape is to be found in many kinds of plant. The topmost, or "leader" shoot releases a hormone which reduces the rate of growth of the side shoots; the whole plant thus takes on the form of a central stem surrounded by branches whose length is related to that of the central stem.

Although the nature of the feedback from the parts to the controlling "centre" or "centres" is largely unknown, its existence is strongly suggested by the facts that wounds heal up and that most plants and some "lower" animals can regenerate whole parts that have been lost. A newt which loses its tail will grow a new one: a crab, caught by a leg, will detach it and then grow a new one; a whole plant may grow out of detached shoot ("cutting") or a small piece of root. Clearly the cells close to the wound regain their ability to divide rapidly and to become differentiated appropriately—an ability which has been lost, or suppressed, by the presence of a complete tail or leg, for example.

In this final section, we have been discussing highly complicated activities of living organisms in which there can be little doubt that control systems are in operation. But we are, as yet, far from having enough knowledge to be able to apply control system theory with any hope of useful results. To know that it is there, however, may help to direct research which will provide that knowledge.

8 ELEMENTARY MATHEMATICS OF SERVO SYSTEMS

(1) LINEAR SYSTEMS. STEP AND RAMP FUNCTION INPUTS

Let the position of the input element at any moment be θ_i, and that of the output element be θ_o. Then the misalignment, θ is defined as $\theta = \theta_i - \theta_o$.

Proportional control

The force exerted by the motor is $K.\theta$, where K is the stiffness.

Pure elastic load on output element. Let the movement of the output element be opposed by a spring which exerts a force which is E times the change in length. Then if the input element is suddenly moved from its initial position through a distance θ_i, the output element will move through a distance θ_o such that the force exerted by the spring is equal to the force exerted by the motor. Thus:

$$K.\theta - E.\theta_o = 0 \qquad (1.1)$$

This is the "governing equation" (loop transfer function) of this very simple system. Replacing θ_o by $(\theta_i - \theta)$, we get:

$$K.\theta - E.\theta_i + E.\theta = 0$$

or

$$\theta = \frac{E}{K+E}\theta_i = \theta_s \qquad (1.2)$$

This gives us the steady state error of the system.

Viscous load on output element. If the output element is moving with a velocity v_o, the load will develop a force, opposing that developed by the motor, which may be written $F.v_o$, where F is the coefficient of viscous resistance.

Let the input element be initially at rest, and then suddenly made to move with a velocity u. Then in the *steady state*, the output element will move with the same velocity, and the force developed by the load will be equal to the force developed by the motor. Thus:

$$K.\theta_s = F.v_o = F.u$$

or
$$\theta_s = (F/K).u \qquad (1.3)$$

The steady state error is thus proportional to the input *velocity*, increases with increase in the output load and decreases with increase in the stiffness of the system.

In the *transient conditions*, the output velocity is approaching the input velocity more or less gradually and is thus varying from moment to moment: in the notation of the infinitesimal calculus, it is written as $(d\theta_o/dt)$. At any moment, the instantaneous force exerted by the motor is equal to the instantaneous viscous force, and the governing equation becomes:

$$K.\theta - F.(d\theta_o/dt) = 0 \qquad (1.4)$$

If θ_o is replaced by $(\theta_i - \theta)$, we get:

$$K.\theta + F.\ (d\theta/dt) = F.\ (d\theta_i/dt) \qquad (1.5)$$

In the steady state, the misalignment is constant, so that $(d\theta/dt)$ $= 0$, and if $(d\theta_i/dt)$ is replaced by u, we get equation 1.3.

The constant K is a measure of the force exerted by the motor per unit change in position of the misalignment element: the constant F is a measure of the force exerted by the viscous load per unit change in velocity, or change in position per unit time. The ratio F/K thus has the dimensions of time and may be replaced by a "time constant", written as T_m. (This time constant lumps together the gain in the controller, the force-excitation relation of the motor, the force-velocity relation of the motor, and the coefficient of friction in the load.) Equation 1.4 thus becomes:

$$\theta - T_m.\ (d\theta_o/dt) = 0 \qquad (1.4a)$$

and equation 1.5 becomes:

$$\theta + T_m.\ (d\theta/dt) = T_m.\ (d\theta_i/dt) \qquad (1.5a)$$

It is convenient to introduce the "differential operator" D, which represents (d/dt), so that equation 1.4a may be written:

$$\theta - T_m.\ D\theta_o = 0 \qquad (1.4b)$$

or
$$\theta_o = \theta/T_m.\ D$$

This governing equation, or loop transfer function, is also an "integrating function"; since integration is the inverse operation of differentiation, $1/D$ is the "integral operator". It is a "first order" equation, since it includes only the first power of D (the first differential coefficient of θ).

Visco-elastic load on output element. The governing equation is a combination of equations 1.1 and 1.4, i.e.:

$$K.\theta - E.\theta_o - F. (d\theta_o/dt) = 0 \qquad (1.6)$$

Putting $F/E = T_o$, the time constant of the load, we get:

$$\theta_o = \frac{T_o}{T_m} \frac{\theta}{(1 + T_o. D)} = G. \frac{\theta}{(1 + T_o. D)} \qquad (1.6a)$$

The ratio T_o/T_m $(=G=K/E)$ defines the output/misalignment ratio in the steady state when $D.\theta_o = 0$, and is sometimes known as the "loop gain".

Solution of first order equations

Suppose that a system with a viscous frictional load is in a steady state, with some finite input displacement, or input velocity, and the input element is then suddenly brought to zero displacement or zero velocity. Equation 1.5, with $(d\theta_i/dt)$ put equal to zero, then shows how the misalignment changes subsequently. Such an equation is known as the "characteristic equation" of the system.

From equation 1.5a, we get: $\theta = -T_m. (d\theta/dt)$

or $\qquad -(1/T_m). dt = (1/\theta). d\theta \qquad (1.7)$

On integration, equation 1.7 becomes:

$$-(t/T_m) = \log_e \theta + \text{a constant} \qquad (1.8)$$

Suppose, as a simple example, that the input is given a displacement h bringing it from $-h$ to zero. Immediately after this, before the output element has begun to move, the misalignment is h. Putting equation 1.8 into another form, we get:

$$\theta = h. \exp (-t/T_m) \qquad (1.8a)$$

where we have put the constant in equation 1.8 equal to $-\log_e h$. When $t = 0$, $\exp (-t/T_m) = 1$, and $\theta = h$, as it should be. When $t = \infty$, $\exp (-t/T_m) = 0$ and $\theta = 0$. The misalignment thus falls "exponentially" towards zero, reaching half way in a time $t_{\frac{1}{2}}$, given by:

$$t_{\frac{1}{2}} = -\log_e (\tfrac{1}{2}) T_m = 0.69 T_m$$

Since the output position θ_o is given by $(\theta_i - \theta)$ and $\theta_i = 0$, we have from equation 1.8a:

$$\theta_o = -h . \exp\ (-t/T_m) \tag{1.9}$$

Alternatively, if θ_i were suddenly increased from 0 to $+h$ and held there, $(d\theta_i/dt)$ is again zero, and we get:

$$\theta_o = h\ [1 - \exp\ (-t/T_m)] \tag{1.10}$$

This is the expression plotted in *Figure 8* (p. 35) as curve (a), h being made equal to 1.

It can easily be shown that equations 1.9 and 1.10 apply also to a system with a visco-elastic load, provided that allowance is made for the steady state error. In equation 1.10, when $t = \infty$, θ_o now becomes $(h - \theta_s)$; using equation 1.2, this becomes: $\theta_o = h . T_o/(T_o + T_m)$, when $t = \infty$.

Suppose, now, that the input is suddenly made to move with a constant velocity u. The misalignment does not now fall exponentially towards 0, but towards the steady state velocity error, θ_s: from equation 1.3, this is given by $T_m . u$. We now find that:

$$\theta = T_m . u . \exp\ (-t/T_m) \tag{1.11}$$

and the output velocity, v_o $(= d\theta_o/dt)$ is given by:

$$v_o = u\ [1 - \exp\ (-t/T_m)] \tag{1.12}$$

Inertia on the output element

In the presence of inertia, part of the force exerted by the motor will be used in accelerating the output element from zero velocity. Since acceleration is rate of change of velocity, we write it as $(dv_o/dt) = (d^2\theta_o/dt^2) = D^2\theta_o$. The governing equation now becomes:

$$K.\theta - (I.D^2\theta_o + F.D\theta_o) = 0 \tag{1.13}$$

(viscous friction is assumed to be present, as well as inertia). This is a "second order" equation, since it contains a term in D^2: its solution will be considered later.

Floating control

Input feed forward. The controller adds to the misalignment signal, sent to the motor, a signal proportional to the velocity of the input element. The governing equation is now:

$$K.\theta + M.D\theta_i - F.D\theta_o = 0$$

This becomes: $(K + F.D)\theta = (F - M). D\theta_i$

or: $$(1 + T_m D)\ \theta = (T_m - T_i). D\theta_i \qquad (1.14)$$

where $T_i = M/K$. In the steady state, when $D\theta = 0$, θ_s will also be zero, whatever the value of $D\theta_i$, provided that $T_i = T_m$.

Integral control. The signal sent to the motor now has added to it a signal proportional to the "time integral" of all past misalignments. The governing equation of the servo system becomes:

$$K.\theta + N.\int\theta.\ dt - F.\ (d\theta_o/dt) = 0 \qquad (1.15)$$

where N is a constant indicating that only part of the whole integrated signal is used. This equation may be written:

$$(K + N/D)\ \theta - F.D\theta_o = 0 \qquad (1.15a)$$

Differentiating equation 1.15 (multiplying equation 1.15a by D), we get:

$$(K.D + N)\ \theta - F.D^2\theta_o = 0$$

This, like the governing equation of the system with output inertia (equation 1.13) is a second order differential equation.

Replacing θ_o by $(\theta_i - \theta)$, we get:

$$(F.D^2 + K.D + N)\theta = F.D^2\theta_i \qquad (1.16)$$

In the steady state, both $D^2\theta$ and $D\theta$ are zero, and with a constant rate of input $D\theta_i$ is constant and thus $D^2\theta_i$ is zero. Hence $\theta_s = 0$. There is no steady state velocity error, but there is an acceleration error if the input rate changes. This can be eliminated, if need be, by adding a second process of integration. The governing equation then becomes of the third order.

Delays

Simple exponential delays. Suppose that a system with an exponential delay is excited by a stimulus θ_e suddenly applied to it. The response, or signal sent out from it, θ_r, will increase at a rate proportional to the difference between θ_e and θ_r at any moment. Thus:

$$(d\theta_r/dt) = (1/T_d).\ (\theta_e - \theta_r)$$

or $$\theta_e = \theta_r + T_d\ (d\theta_r/dt) \qquad (1.17)$$

$$= \theta_r\ (1 + T_d.\ D) \qquad (1.17a)$$

where T_d is the time constant of the delay. Hence the transfer function of the delay is:

$$\theta_r = \frac{\theta_e}{(1 + T_d . D)} \qquad (1.18)$$

If we write equation 1.17 as:

$$(\theta_e - \theta_r) = T_d \ (d\theta_r/dt)$$

it has the same form as equation 1.7, $(\theta_e - \theta_r)$ being analogous to $(\theta_i - \theta_o)$ or θ. The solution to equation 1.17, by analogy, is thus:

$$(\theta_e - \theta_r) = \theta_e . \exp \ (-t/T_d)$$
$$\theta_r = \theta_e \ [1 - \exp \ (-t/T_d)] \qquad (1.19)$$

This, being the same as equation 1.10, is also represented by curve (a) in *Figure 8*.

Proportional control system with a single exponential delay. The force exerted by the motor of the simple servo system whose governing equation is given by equation 1.4 or 1.4a, will now be proportional to the output (response) of the delay, θ_r, the input (stimulus) to the delay, θ_e, being the "true" misalignment $(\theta_i - \theta_o)$: this is so whether the delay is in the receptor, the controller or in the motor (effector) itself. Thus we may write equation 1.4b as:

$$\theta_r = T_m . \ D\theta_o$$

Inserting equation 1.18, so as to replace θ_r by θ_e $(=\theta)$, we get:

$$\theta = T_m \ (D + T_d . \ D^2) \ \theta_o \qquad (1.20)$$

The governing equation is once more of the second order. Replacing θ_o by $(\theta_i - \theta)$, we get:

$$(T_m T_d . \ D^2 + T_m . \ D + 1) \ \theta = T_m . \ D\theta_i + T_m T_d . \ D^2 \theta_i \qquad (1.21)$$

Two independent exponential delays in series. We now have:

$$\theta_r = \frac{\theta_e}{(1 + T_d . \ D) \ (1 + q T_d . \ D)} = \frac{\theta_e}{1 + (1 + q) \ T_d . \ D + q T_d^2 . \ D^2} \qquad (1.22)$$

the second delay having a time constant which is q times that of the first. This again is a second order equation, whose solution will be considered later.

Complex exponential delays. If I is the inertia of the moving system in the measuring device (the mass of the liquid column of a manometer, for example), F is the friction in the system (the viscous resistance to flow of the manometer fluid) and K is the restoring force per unit deflection (equal to g (981 cm/sec^2) in a manometer), we have:

$$(I.D^2+F.D)\ \theta_r = K\ (\theta_e - \theta_r)$$

or
$$\theta_r = \frac{\theta_e}{(I/K).D^2+(F/K).D+1} \qquad (1.23)$$

This equation is of the same form as the governing equation of the servo system with inertia, considered above, when θ_r is replaced by θ_o and $(\theta_e - \theta_r)$ is replaced by θ.

Finite delays. Although these seem simpler than exponential delays, they cannot be handled mathematically so easily. If the stimulus to a finite delay, $\theta_e(t)$, is some function of time, then the response, $\theta_r(t)$, will be the same function with all the times reduced by the fixed delay time T_f. Thus:

$$\theta_r(t) = \theta_e\ (t - T_f)$$

If we expand the right-hand side of this equation by means of Taylor's series, we get:

$$\theta_r(t) = \theta_e(t)\ (1 - T_f.\,D + \tfrac{1}{2}\ T_f^2.\,D^2 - \tfrac{1}{6}\ T_f^3.\,D^3 + \ .\ \ .\ \ .)\ \text{where}$$

$\theta_e(t).\ T_f.\ D = T_f\ (d\theta_e(t)/dt)$.

We see from this that the transfer function of a finite delay is:

$$\theta_r = \theta_e \exp(-T_f.D) \qquad (1.24)$$

Now suppose that we have several simple exponential delays in series; the transfer function of the whole series will be the product of all the individual transfer functions. Thus, from equation 1.18, if there are n similar delays:

$$\theta_r = \frac{\theta_e}{(1 + T_d.\ D)^n}$$

Also, from the definition of the exponential series, we have:

$$\frac{1}{\exp(T_f.\ D)} = Lt_{n \to \infty}\ \frac{1}{\left(1 + \dfrac{T_f.\ D}{n}\right)^n}$$

This is clearly the same as the transfer function of n exponential delays each with a time constant equal to T_f/n. Thus a finite delay is theoretically equivalent to an infinite succession of simple exponential delays which do not interact with one another. For practical purposes, it is often sufficient to limit the number to three, each with a time constant which is one-third of the finite delay time; this, however, is complicated enough. There are graphical methods which make the handling of finite delays relatively easy, as we shall see later.

Damping

Output velocity feedback. A signal proportional to the output velocity, say $T_o.(d\theta_o/dt)$, is fed to the controller, where it is subtracted from the misalignment signal, and the difference sent on to the motor. In the absence of any viscous load, the motor will speed up until it is exerting no force, and the signal from the controller vanishes. Thus:

$$K\ [\theta - T_o\ (d\theta_o/dt)] = 0 \qquad (1.25)$$

This equation is of the same form as equation 1.4a, and its solution will be given by equations 1.9 to 1.12 with T_o in place of T_m. We can, moreover, imagine that the particular part of the controller which receives the signal proportional to the output velocity, and subtracts it from the misalignment signal, is moved into the motor. The fact that the force exerted by the motor falls as the speed of movement rises may be attributed to an inherent output velocity feedback. The transfer function of such a motor will be of the same form as equations 1.4a and 1.25. (In most practical motors, however, including living muscles, the inherent feedback is not linear—i.e. the coefficient T_o in equation 1.25 is not constant.)

Error rate (derivative) control. A device is inserted which finds the rate of change of the misalignment, and adds its signal to the misalignment signal. The governing equation of the servo system will then be:

$$K.\ \theta + L.\ D\theta - F.\ D\theta_o = 0 \qquad (1.26)$$

where L defines the amount of error rate signal sent to the motor.

In practice, the rate measuring device will be associated with a delay. In the simplest case, this will be a simple exponential delay, and the transfer function of the rate measuring device will be:

$$\theta_r = \frac{T_a . D}{1 + T_{ad} . D} \theta_e \tag{1.27}$$

where T_a is the time constant of the differentiating (rate measuring) part of the device ($=L/K$ in equation 1.26) and T_{ad} is the time constant of the associated delay. The governing equation (1.26) may thus be written:

$$\theta_o = \frac{1}{T_m . D} . \frac{(1 + T_a . D)}{(1 + T_{ad} . D)} \theta \tag{1.28}$$

The delay, however, may be more elaborate than this, and the denominator of equations 1.27 and 1.28 will then contain higher powers of D.

Some kinds of practical device, which provide directly the value of $(1 + T_a . D)/(1 + T_{ad} . D)$, also multiply the signal by the ratio T_{ad}/T_a. It is desirable, in general, to make this ratio as small as possible (in the limit, if $T_{ad} = T_a$, there would be no error signal at all). The consequent reduction in size of the signal is equivalent to increasing the value of T_m ($=F/K$): this would increase the steady state error (equations 1.3 and 1.5a). In order to avoid this, it is usual to add some extra amplification in the controller, so that the signals are all multiplied by T_a/T_{ad}. The device is then described as "gain compensated".

Solution of second order equations. Oscillation

The characteristic equations describing the transient behaviour of the systems with viscous load or output velocity feedback, and with (a) proportional control and inertia (equation 1.13), (b) proportional control and one simple exponential delay (equation 1.20), and (c) integral control as well as proportional control (equation 1.16), all take the same form: this is the same, also, as that of the transfer functions of two simple exponential delays in series (equation 1.22) and of a complex exponential delay (equation 1.23), when θ_e is suddenly reduced to zero. The solutions of all these equations, therefore, may be found in the same way. For reasons which will appear later, we will put them into the general form:

$$(D^2 + 2\zeta\omega_n D + \omega_n{}^2)\theta = 0 \tag{1.29}$$

F

Solution of this equation is not difficult, provided that it is linear, and ζ and ω_n are constants. It is a quadratic equation in D and, according to the rules for solving quadratic equations, the roots are given by:

$$D = \frac{-2\zeta\omega_n \pm \sqrt{4\zeta^2\,\omega_n{}^2 - 4\omega_n{}^2}}{2} = \omega_n(-\zeta \pm \sqrt{\zeta^2 - 1})$$

The form of the solution depends on whether ζ is greater or less than 1, and whether $\sqrt{\zeta^2 - 1}$ is "real" or "imaginary".

(1) $\zeta = 1$. This is the simplest case, since $(D + \omega_n)$ is a factor in the quadratic equation, and we have:

$$(D + \omega_n)\theta = 0 \quad \text{or} \quad \theta = -(1/\omega_n).\,(d\theta/dt)$$

Comparison of this equation with equation 1.7, the solution of which is equation 1.8a, shows that its solution is:

$$\theta = A.\,\exp(-\omega_n t)$$

where A is some constant depending on the initial conditions just before θ_i is reduced to zero. There must, however, be two solutions to every quadratic equation: the other one is:

$$\theta = Bt.\,\exp(-\omega_n t)$$

That this is indeed a solution can be proved by finding $D^2\theta$ and $D\theta$ and inserting these, together with θ in the quadratic equation (1.29), which then adds up to zero. The full solution is thus:

$$\theta = \exp(-\omega_n t).\,(A + Bt) \tag{1.30}$$

Suppose, as before, that at time 0, the input is given a sudden displacement h: when $t = 0$, $\theta = h$ and $D\theta = 0$. From equation 1.30, putting $t = 0$, we find $A = h$. By differentiating equation 1.30, equating this to zero and putting $t = 0$, we find $0 = -\omega_n h + B$, or $B = \omega_n h$. Thus the complete solution is:

$$\theta = h.\,\exp(-\omega_n t).\,(1 + \omega_n t) \tag{1.30a}$$

Moreover, since $\theta_o = \theta_i - \theta$, we have:

$$\theta_o = h\,[1 - \exp(-\omega_n t).\,(1 + \omega_n t)] \tag{1.30b}$$

This expression is plotted in *Figure 8* (p. 35) as curve (b), when $h = 1$. It also defines the relation between θ_r and θ_e given by two equal exponential delays in series $(q = 1)$ after putting $\omega_n = 1/T_d$.

(2) ζ is greater than 1. The solution, by analogy, will be:
$$\theta = \exp\ (-\zeta\omega_n t)\ [A.\ \exp\ (\omega_n t.\sqrt{\zeta^2-1}) + B.\ \exp\ (-\omega_n t\sqrt{\zeta^2-1})] \tag{1.31}$$

From this expression, using the methods of the previous paragraph, we can plot the transfer function of two exponential delays with different time constants when given a step function stimulus.

(3) ζ is less than 1. We cannot now evaluate $\sqrt{\zeta^2-1}$: we have to introduce the operator j (or i) which is $\sqrt{-1}$, and express the solution as a "complex number". (Mathematicians generally use i, engineers j; we will use j in order to avoid any possible confusion with symbols representing the input to a servo system.) In equation 1.31, therefore, $\sqrt{\zeta^2-1}$ is replaced by $j\sqrt{1-\zeta^2}$. For simplicity, we will put $\zeta\omega_n = a$, and $\omega_n\sqrt{1-\zeta^2} = b$. Then:

$$\theta = \exp\ (-a.\,t)\ [A.\ \exp\ (jbt) + B.\ \exp\ (-jbt)] \tag{1.32}$$

But $\exp\ (jbt) = \cos\ bt + j.\ \sin\ bt$
and $\exp\ (-jbt) = \cos\ bt - j.\ \sin\ bt$
(the proof of this may be found in books on mathematics).

$$\left.\begin{aligned} \text{Thus:}\quad \theta &= \exp\ (-at)\ [(A+B)\ \cos\ bt + j\ (A-B)\ \sin\ bt] \\ &= \exp\ (-at).\ (E.\ \cos\ bt + j.F\ \sin\ bt) \\ &= G.\ \exp\ (-at).\ \cos\ (bt + \Psi) \end{aligned}\right\} \tag{1.33}$$

Since A and B are arbitrary constants, depending on the initial and final conditions of the system, $(A+B)$ and $(A-B)$ may be replaced by two other constants E and F, and these by two others G and Ψ, where $E = G.\ \cos\ \Psi$ and $F = -G.\ \sin\ \Psi$.

If $\zeta = 0$, $a = 0$ and $b = \omega_m$. The expression for θ is that of a simple harmonic motion and the value of θ oscillates between $+G$ and $-G$ indefinitely as $(\omega_m t + \Psi)$ increases from 0 to π, to 2π radians etc.: $\omega_n/2\pi$ is thus the frequency of the oscillations, and this is why ω_n was introduced earlier on.

If ζ is not zero, but is less than 1, the amplitude of the oscillations dies away exponentially with time, the time constant being $1/a\ (=1/\zeta\omega_n)$, and their frequency is $\omega_n\sqrt{1-\zeta^2}$. There is hunting, and the number of overshoots and undershoots with an amplitude **greater** than is acceptable becomes smaller as ζ becomes greater (more nearly 1). ζ is thus the "damping coefficient", and was introduced for this reason. If ζ is less than 0, the damping is negative and the amplitude of the oscillations increases progressively with time. If $\zeta = 1$, the system just fails to oscillate, the damping is "critical" and θ decays exponentially towards zero as t approaches infinity. If ζ is greater than 1, the system is "over-damped" and the time constant of the decay becomes greater (the decay is slower) the greater the value of ζ.

Consider, for example, a proportional control system with a viscous load on the output (or output velocity feedback) and an exponential delay. We see, by comparing equation 1.29 with equation 1.21, that $\omega_n{}^2 = 1/T_m T_d$ ($= K/F \cdot T_d$) and that $2\zeta\omega_n = 1/T_d$; thus $2\zeta = \sqrt{T_m/T_d}$. Similar expressions for ω_n and ζ can be obtained for systems in which there is inertia on the output element, instead of an exponential delay, and for systems in which integral control has been added. Further, from equation 1.3 (p. 152), the steady state error, θ_s, is $(F/K) \cdot u = T_m \cdot u$, and is thus also $(2\zeta/\omega_n) \cdot u$. This, however, holds only when all the damping is on the output element. Suppose we add some error rate control, and assume, for simplicity, that we have an "ideal" differentiating device. We see, by comparing equation 1.26a with equation 1.4b, that in the governing equation θ must be replaced by $\theta(1 + T_a \cdot D)$. Correspondingly, in the characteristic equation (equation 1.29 with $D\theta_i = D^2\theta_i = 0$), the coefficient of $D\theta$ will be $(T_a + T_m)$ and the damping coefficient ζ will be increased by $T_a/2\sqrt{T_m T_d}$. In the steady state, however, since $D\theta = 0$, the introduction of T_a has no effect; $\theta_s = T_m \cdot u$ as before and is not directly proportional to ζ.

The curves in *Figure 10* (p. 41) are plotted from equations 1.30, 1.31 and 1.33, introducing the limiting conditions that when t approaches infinity, $\theta = \theta_s = (2\zeta/\omega_n) \cdot u$; and that when $t = 0$, $\theta = 0$ and $D\theta = D\theta_i = u$. From these limiting conditions, the values of the constants A and B (or E and F) can be found. Clearly, if θ is multiplied by ω_n/u, when plotting the curves, θ_s (in these units) depends only on ζ: and if we use $\omega_n t$ as unit of time, the time constants of the exponential decays and the duration of one cycle of oscillation become independent of the particular parameters of the system. The curves are thus "dimensionless".

Solution of third and higher order equations

As a somewhat more complicated example, we may take a system which has integral control as well as an exponential delay and output damping. Its transient behaviour will be described by an equation similar to equation 1.29 but with an additional term in $D^3\theta$: there will be three roots, two of which may be complex, and the solution may be written:

$$\theta = C. \exp\ (-mt) + \exp\ (-at)\ [E.\ \cos\ bt + jF.\ \sin\ bt] \qquad (1.34)$$

The way in which θ changes after the input is suddenly given a constant velocity is shown in *Figure 11*. The constant m defines the rate at which the misalignment is brought to zero by the integral control—i.e. the line PQR in *Figure 11*; b and a, as before, define the frequency of the oscillations and the rate at which they are damped out. All three constants depend on the values of N, F, K, and T_d in the governing equation in rather complicated ways.

Addition of further components results in equations of even higher orders: the higher the order the more difficult and laborious is the complete solution of the equation. But we get some idea as to how the system will behave in the transient conditions without a complete solution. If b_0, b_1, b_2, b_3 and b_4 are the coefficients of D°, D^1, D^2, D^3, and D^4 in the governing equation, the system will be stable, in the sense of not going into permanent oscillation, if the "Routh-Hurwitz" criteria are satisfied. These are:

for a 3rd order system: $b_1\ b_2 > b_0\ b_3$
for a 4th order system: $b_1\ b_2\ b_3 > b_0\ b_3{}^2 + b_4\ b_1{}^2$

Analogous criteria can be obtained for systems of even higher orders. In practice, if the amount of hunting is to be acceptable, "factors of safety" must be introduced: these have been calculated so as to give reasonable values of the maximum overshoot, but depend on the nature of the equation; they may be found in more advanced books on control systems.

(2) LINEAR SYSTEMS.   SIMPLE HARMONIC INPUTS.   FREQUENCY
RESPONSE CURVES

A simple harmonic motion is often known as a "sinusoidal" oscillation. This is because the instantaneous position of, say, the input element of a control system at any time t after starting the motion can be defined by an expression such as: $\theta_i = |\theta_i|\ \sin\ \omega t$. It suits the treatment adopted earlier in this chapter, however, if we write:

$$\theta_i = |\theta_i|\ \cos\ \omega t \qquad (2.1)$$

This equation defines the following relations between t and θ_i: $t=0$, $\theta_i=|\theta_i|$; $t=\pi/2\omega$ $(\omega t=90°)$, $\theta_i=0$; $t=\pi/\omega$ $(\omega t= 180°)$, $\theta_i=-|\theta_i|$; $t=3\pi/2\omega$ $(\omega t=270°)$, $\theta_i=0$; and $t=2\pi/\omega$ $(\omega t=360°)$, $\theta_i=|\theta_i|$. Thus θ_i oscillates between $+|\theta_i|$ and $-|\theta_i|$, so that $|\theta_i|$ is the amplitude; and $2\pi/\omega$ is the time taken by one complete oscillation, so that ω is the "circular frequency" $(=2\pi f$ where f is the frequency in cycles per second).

The output of the control system is also a simple harmonic motion with the same frequency as the input, but with a different amplitude and different phase. Thus the instantaneous position of the output element is defined by:

$$\theta_o=|\theta_o| \cos (\omega t+\Psi) \qquad (2.2)$$

The vector defining the amplitude and phase of the input motion is used, a "reference vector", of unit length and zero phase, drawn along the positive "real" axis: this means, in effect, that the motion is plotted at the moment when $t=0$ (or $2\pi/\omega$ etc.). The vector representing the amplitude and phase of the output motion has a length $|\theta_o|$ and at this moment is inclined at an angle Ψ to the positive "real" axis: in *Figure 37* it is represented by the vector $\overline{OB}$. This vector may be regarded as the sum of two other vectors, one along the "real" axis, $\overline{OC}$, of length a $(=|\theta_o| \cos \Psi)$ and the other parallel to the "imaginary" axis of length b $(=|\theta_o| \sin \Psi)$; but it must be made clear that the latter is at right angles to the former. This is done, as already discussed, by multiplying it by the operator j. Thus:

$$\theta_o=|\theta_o| (\cos \Psi+j. \sin \Psi) \qquad (2.3)$$

It can be shown mathematically that equation 2.3 may also be written as:

$$\theta_o=|\theta_o| \exp (j.\Psi) \qquad (2.3a)$$

(The proof of this is simple but rather lengthy.)

Similarly, if an excitatory stimulus is given to some particular component of the servo system, its amplitude may be taken as unity and its phase as zero. The response of the component will then have an amplitude $|\theta_r|$ and phase angle Ψ, so that the transfer function may be written:

$$\theta_r=|\theta_r| \exp (j.\Psi)$$

If, now, there is also a second component whose transfer function is: $\theta_r{}^1 = |\theta_r|^1 \exp. (j\Psi^1)$, and it is given as stimulus the response

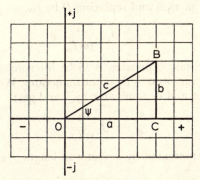

FIGURE 37   *Representation of vectors as complex numbers.*

The horizontal (x) axes are the "real" axes, positive to the right, negative to the left: the vertical (y) axes are the "imaginary" axes, $+j$ upwards and $-j$ downwards. The vector $\overline{OB}$, of length c and phase angle Ψ may be defined by the sum of the two vectors $\overline{OC}$ (length a) and $\overline{BC}$ (length b) at right angles. Thus $\bar{c} = (a+jb) = c$ (cos $\Psi + j$sin Ψ).

of the first component, the transfer function of both together is:

$$\theta_r.\ \theta_r{}^1 = |\theta_r|.\ |\theta_r|^1 \exp (j.\Psi).\ \exp (j.\Psi^1)$$
$$= |\theta_r|.\ |\theta_r|^1 \exp j. (\Psi + \Psi^1) \qquad (2.4)$$

This is the derivation of the rule for multiplying several vectors together.

Returning to equation 2.1, and differentiating it with respect to time, we get:

$$d\theta_i/dt = D\theta_i = -\omega|\theta_i| \sin \omega t = \omega|\theta_i| \cos (\omega t + 90°)$$
$$= j\omega\theta_i \qquad (2.5)$$

Differentiation of the vector has the effect of rotating it through 90° (giving it a phase lead of 90°), and thus of multiplying it by j. From equation 2.5, we see that when using simple harmonic motions as inputs, the operator D can be replaced by $j\omega$; D^2 thus becomes $-\omega^2$, and so on. This is one of the great advantages of using simple harmonic motions for studying the behaviour of servo systems.

Transfer functions with simple harmonic motion inputs

The motor with inherent damping or a viscous load. Turning back to equation 1.4*b* (p. 152) and replacing D by $j\omega$, we get:

$$\theta_o = \frac{1}{j\omega T_m}\,\theta \qquad (2.6)$$

When an algebraic expression is to be interpreted as a vector, the operator j must occur only in the numerator. We thus multiply both numerator and denominator by j, and get:

$$\frac{\theta_o}{\theta} = -j\cdot\frac{1}{\omega T_m} \qquad (2.6a)$$

Thus θ_o/θ is represented by a vector of length $1/\omega T_m$ along the $-j$ axis.

For the logarithmic plots, we have:

$$\log_{10}(|\theta_o|/|\theta|) = -\log_{10}(\omega T_m)$$
$$\text{and} \qquad \lambda = -20\log_{10}(\omega T_m) \qquad (2.6b)$$

Thus λ changes by 20 dB for each decade change in frequency, or by $0.3 \times 20 = 6$ dB for each octave change: λ is zero when $\omega = 1/T_m$.

Simple exponential delay. Similarly, from equation 1.18 (p. 156), we get:

$$\theta_r = \frac{1}{(1+j\omega T_d)}\cdot\theta_e \qquad (2.7)$$

This must be re-arranged so that j occurs only in the numerator, and so that all the terms preceded by j are separated from those without j. This is done by multiplying numerator and denominator by the "conjugate vector" of the denominator—i.e. the vector with the sign in front of j reversed, in this case $(1-j\omega T_d)$. We then get:

$$\frac{\theta_r}{\theta_e} = \frac{1}{(1+\omega^2 T_d^2)} - j\cdot\frac{\omega T_d}{(1+\omega^2 T_d^2)} \qquad (2.8)$$

When $\omega T_d = 0$, the value of this expression is 1; when $\omega T_d = \infty$ its value is 0; and when $\omega T_d = 1$, its value is $(\frac{1}{2} - j\cdot\frac{1}{2})$—i.e. the vector is the hypotenuse of a right-angled triangle whose two other sides are of length $\frac{1}{2}$, one being along the positive "real" axis and the other along the $-j$ axis. We may repeat this process for a number of different values of ωT_d, but this is not necessary since the shape of the locus can be calculated algebraically. From *Figure 37*, we see that when a vector of length c and phase angle Ψ is represented as the sum of two vectors, $a + j.b$, we have:

$$\left. \begin{array}{c} c = \sqrt{a^2 + b^2} \\ \tan \Psi = b/a \end{array} \right\} \qquad (2.9)$$

Writing equation 2.8 as $a - j.b$, we see that $b/a = \omega T_d$, and

$$b = \frac{b/a}{1 + (b/a)^2} = \frac{ab}{a^2 + b^2}.$$ Hence: $a^2 + b^2 - a = 0$, or $(a - \tfrac{1}{2})^2 + b^2 = \tfrac{1}{4}$.

This is the equation of a circle, with radius $\tfrac{1}{2}$ and centred at point $(\tfrac{1}{2}, j.0)$. Since the phase angle is always negative (the response lags behind the stimulus), only the lower half (on the $-j$ side of the positive axis) is applicable.

For the logarithmic plots, applying equations 2.9 to equation 2.8, we get:

$$\frac{|\theta_r|}{|\theta_e|} = \frac{1}{\sqrt{1 + \omega^2 T_d^2}}$$

$$\tan \Psi = -\omega T_d$$

Thus: $\qquad \lambda = -10 \log_{10}(1 + \omega^2 T_d^2) \qquad (2.10)$

When ωT_d is small, approaching zero, λ also approaches zero: when ωT_d is very large, approaching infinity, λ approaches $-20 \log_{10}(\omega T_d)$, or a line sloping at -6 dB/octave. On extrapolation of this line, λ becomes 0 when $\omega T_d = 1$: the two asymptotes intersect when $\omega = 1/T_d$, and this, therefore is the corner frequency. But from equation 2.10, when $\omega T_d = 1$, $\lambda = -10 \log_{10}(2)$ or -3 dB, and this is the divergence at the corner. Divergences at other values of the frequency may easily be calculated in the same way.

The phase angle approaches 0 as ω approaches 0, and approaches $\tan^{-1}(-\infty) = -90°$ as ω approaches ∞: when $\omega = 1/T_d$, $\tan \Psi = -1$ and $\Psi = -45°$. Values of Ψ for other values of ω may easily be calculated with the aid of a table of tangents.

The motor with a visco-elastic load. The transfer function (equation 1.6a) is identical in form with that of an exponential delay (equation 1.18) except for the presence of the "loop gain", G.

F*

The transfer locus will have the same shape as that of an exponential delay, but when $\omega T_o = 0$, θ_0/θ is not 1, but is G: the radius of the semi-circle will be $G/2$ instead of $1/2$.

For the logarithmic plots, we have:

$$\tan \Psi = -\omega T_o$$
$$\lambda = -10 \log_{10} (1 + \omega^2 T_o^2) + 20 \log_{10} G$$

The phase line is the same as that of an exponential delay. When ωT_o is very large, the asymptote of the attenuation line again has a slope of -6 dB/octave: but when ωT_o is very small, λ approaches $20 \log_{10} G$ instead of 0. The low frequency attenuation line has zero slope, but is shifted by $20 \log_{10} G$ dB.

Finite delay. On replacing D in equation 1.24 (p. 157) by $j\omega$, we get:
$$\theta_r = \exp (-j\omega T_f). \ \theta_e \qquad (2.11)$$

or
$$\frac{\theta_r}{\theta_e} = \cos \omega T_f - j. \sin \omega T_f \text{ (compare equations 2.3}$$

and 2.3a). By making ωT_f successively 0, π, 2π etc. and plotting the vectors, this can be seen to represent a vector of unit length which rotates clockwise as ω increases. The transfer locus is thus a circle about the origin, with unit radius. The attenuation is zero at all frequencies, and for the phase angle, we have:

$$\tan \Psi = \frac{-\sin \omega T_f}{\cos \omega T_f} = -\tan \omega T_f$$

Thus $\Psi = -\omega T_f$. When $\omega = 1/T_f$, $\Psi = -1$ radian, or $-57.3°$.

Phase advancing (differentiating) component. From equations 1.27 and 1.28 (p. 159), the transfer function of an "ideal" device which differentiates the signal and adds the result to the signal itself, may be written:

$$\theta_r = (1 + j\omega T_a) \ \theta_e \qquad (2.12)$$

Since this is the inverse of the transfer function of a simple exponential delay (equation 2.7) the transfer locus will be the upper half (on the $+j$ side of the positive axis) of the circle with radius $\frac{1}{2}$ and centred at $(\frac{1}{2}, j.0)$, as already deduced on p. 167.

For the logarithmic plots, similarly, we have:

$$\lambda = 10 \log_{10} (1 + \omega^2 T_a^2)$$

When ω approaches 0, λ also approaches 0; and when ω is very large, λ approaches the asymptote given by: $\lambda = 20 \log_{10} (\omega T_a)$, or a line inclined at $+6$ dB/octave. The phase angles will be the same as those of the exponential delay, but positive instead of negative.

For the "practical" device which introduces an exponential delay, we have:

$$\theta_r = \frac{1 + j\omega T_a}{1 + j\omega T_{ad}} \cdot \theta_a \qquad (2.13)$$

(assuming either that there is no loss of signal, or that there is ("gain compensation"). Multiplying numerator and denominator by $(1 - j\omega T_{ad})$ we get:

$$\frac{\theta_r}{\theta_e} = \frac{(1 + j\omega T_a)\ (1 - j\omega T_{ad})}{1 + \omega^2 T_{ad}^2}$$

$$= \frac{1 + \omega^2 T_a T_{ad}}{1 + \omega^2 T_{ad}^2} + j \cdot \frac{\omega (T_a - T_{ad})}{1 + \omega^2 T_{ad}^2} \qquad (2.13a)$$

In order to find the shape of the transfer locus, we write, as before, equation 2.13a in the form $a + j.b$. From the first term in equation 2.13a, we first find an expression for ω^2 in terms of a, T_a and T_{ad}. This is then substituted in the expression for b^2 deduced from the second term. Putting $T_{ad}/T_a = a$, and after some algebraic manipulation, we find:

$$a^2 - a\ (1/a + 1)\ + b^2 = -1/a$$

or $\left(a - \frac{1/a + 1}{2}\right)^2 + b^2 = -1/a + \left(\frac{1/a + 1}{2}\right)^2 = \left(\frac{1/a - 1}{2}\right)^2$

Thus the locus is a circle, with radius $\frac{1}{2} (1/a - 1)$ and centre on the positive axis distant $\frac{1}{2} (1/a + 1)$ from the origin. With an uncompensated loss of gain by the factor a, the radius becomes $\frac{1}{2} (1 - a)$ and the centre is distant $\frac{1}{2} (1 + a)$ from the origin.

For any given value of ω, the phase angle is given by:

$$\tan \Psi = \frac{\omega (T_a - T_{ad})}{1 + \omega^2 T_a T_{ad}}$$

By finding $d\Psi/d\omega$ and equating to zero, we find that there is a maximum value of Ψ when $\omega^2 T_a$. $T_{ad} = \omega^2 T_a^2$. $a = 1$. Thus

$\omega_{max} \cdot T_a = 1/\sqrt{a}$, or $\omega_{max} = 1/\sqrt{T_a T_{ad}}$. Inserting this in the equation for tan Ψ, and simplifying, we get:

$$\sin \Psi_{max} = \frac{1-a}{1+a} \qquad (2.14)$$

The attenuation and phase lines corresponding to the transfer function given in equation 2.13a are best derived graphically from the curves corresponding to the two separate transfer functions, as has been done in *Figure 20* (p. 65). If there had been an uncompensated loss of gain by the factor T_{ad}/T_a, the attenuation lines would all be moved downwards through 20 $\log_{10}$ (T_{ad}/T_a) dB, but the phase lines would remain unchanged.

Overall transfer function of a system capable of oscillation

The loop transfer function of the system with a simple exponential delay and a motor with output damping, as plotted in *Figures 14 (c)* and *16* (pp. 51, 55) is found by multiplying together the two separate transfer functions, given in equations 2.7 and 2.6. This gives:

$$\theta_0 = \frac{1}{T_m \ (j\omega - T_d \omega^2)} \cdot \theta$$

For the overall transfer function, we put $\theta = \theta_i - \theta_0$, which gives:

$$\frac{\theta_0}{\theta_i} = \frac{1}{-\omega^2 T_m T_d + j\omega T_m + 1}$$

This may be converted into the more general form, applicable for example to systems with output inertia and to systems with integral control, by putting $T_m T_d = 1/\omega_n^2$ and $1/T_m = 2\zeta\omega_n$ (compare p. 159). It is rather more convenient, now, to replace $1/\omega_n$ by T_n, the natural period of the system. We then get:

$$\frac{\theta_0}{\theta_i} = \frac{1}{-\omega^2 T_n^2 + 2j\omega\zeta T_n + 1} \qquad (2.15)$$

(This is essentially the same as the transfer function of a complex exponential delay (equation 1.23) when D is replaced by $j\omega$.)

The amplitude ratio (dynamic magnification) of this closed loop system is:

$$\frac{|\theta_o|}{|\theta_i|} = \frac{1}{\sqrt{(1 - \omega^2 T_n^2)^2 + 4\zeta^2 \omega^2 T_n^2}} \qquad (2.16)$$

The phase angle is:

$$\Psi = \tan^{-1} \frac{-2\zeta\omega T_n}{(1 - \omega^2 T_n^2)} \qquad (2.17)$$

When ω approaches o, $|\theta_o|/|\theta_i|$ approaches 1, so that the attenuation λ approaches o. When ω becomes very large, the only significant term is $\sqrt{(-\omega^2 T_n^2)^2}$ and λ approaches $-40 \log_{10} (\omega T_n)$: the asymptote is thus a line inclined downwards with a slope of -12 dB/octave.

The corner frequency is when $\omega = 1/T_n$, and the frequency of the applied simple harmonic motion is equal to the natural frequency of the system. At this frequency:

$$\tan \Psi = -\frac{2\zeta}{(1-1)} = -\infty : \text{ or } \Psi = -90°$$

and:

$$\frac{|\theta_o|}{|\theta_i|} = \frac{1}{\sqrt{4\zeta^2}} = \frac{1}{2\zeta} : \text{ so that } \lambda = -20 \log_{10} (2\zeta)$$

The dynamic magnification will have a maximum value at some particular frequency if the denominator of equation 2.16 has a minimum value. By differentiating this denominator with respect to ω we find that there is a "resonance" frequency, at which the dynamic magnification has a maximum value, given by: $\omega_r = (\sqrt{1 - 2\zeta^2})/T_n$. This, however, has no real value, and there will be no maximum of the dynamic magnification, unless $\zeta^2 < 0.5$, or $\zeta < 0.7$. Substituting the value of ω_r in equation 2.16, we find that the maximum value of the dynamic magnification is given by:

$$\left(\frac{|\theta_o|}{|\theta_i|}\right)_r = \frac{1}{(2\zeta\sqrt{1-\zeta^2})} : \text{ or } \lambda_r = -20 \log_{10} (2\zeta\sqrt{1-\zeta^2}).$$

Graphical construction of the overall transfer locus from the loop transfer locus

For each value of the frequency, the vector representing the

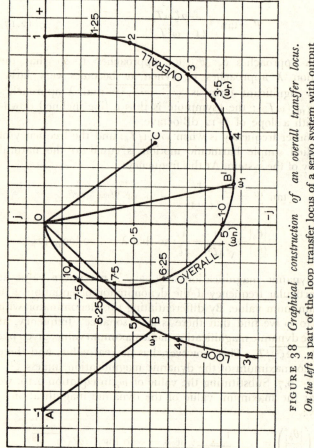

FIGURE 38 *Graphical construction of an overall transfer locus.*
On the left is part of the loop transfer locus of a servo system with output damping and a simple exponential delay, as drawn in *Figure 14 (c)* (p. 51)
On the right is the corresponding overall transfer locus. The method of construction is described in the text.

output/input ratio (θ_o/θ_i) must be discovered from that representing the output/misalignment ratio (θ_o/θ) as plotted. The procedure is illustrated in *Figure 38*. On the left is part of the loop transfer locus as drawn in *Figure 14 (c)* (p. 51). The vector $\overline{OB}$ represents θ_o for some particular frequency ω_1 ($=4.5$ in the diagram). Let A be the point $(-1, j.0)$, so that the vector $\overline{OA}$ is $-\theta$ (θ is made equal to 1 by definition).

Now $-\theta = \theta_o - \theta_i$

Also, by vector addition: $\overline{OA} = \overline{OB} + \overline{BA}$

Thus: $\overline{BA} = -\theta_i$, or $\overline{AB} = \theta_i$

$\overline{OC}$, drawn parallel to $\overline{AB}$, thus represents θ_i, and the phase angle between θ_o and θ_i is the angle COB, which is equal to the angle OBA. For the overall transfer locus, therefore, the vector $\overline{OB^1}$ is drawn with a length equal to the ratio OB/AB ($|\theta_o|/|\theta_i|$), and making an angle to the positive axis equal to the angle OBA. The process is repeated for as many different frequencies as may be necessary.

(3) NON-LINEAR SYSTEMS. PHASE-PLANE TRAJECTORIES

In order to plot a phase-plane trajectory, it is necessary to derive a relation between the misalignment (θ) and the misalignment velocity (v).

On-off control

Let the motor exert a constant force P and let the output element have a load with a moment of inertia I and a viscous friction coefficient F. Then the equation of motion of the output element will be:

$$\pm P = I.D^2\theta_o + F.D\theta_o = I.\frac{dv_o}{dt} + F.v_o = \pm F.v_m \qquad (3.1)$$

In the limit, if the motor were allowed to run for a sufficiently long time, $D^2\theta_o$ would become zero, and v_o would reach a maximum value v_m. Thus $\pm P$ may be replaced by $\pm F.v_m$. The same equation will apply if there is an exponential delay at the motor instead of inertia on the output element, but I will be replaced by $F.T_d$, where T_d is the time constant of the delay. P and v_m will be positive when v_o and θ_o are increasing: they will be negative after the system has overshot the dead zone, reversed excitation occurs while the system is in motion and v_o is first reduced to zero and then increased in the opposite direction.

Step function input (sudden displacement). The system is given a misalignment, and when it is released, the input velocity (v_i) is zero, so that $v_o = -v$ and $dv_o/dt = -dv/dt$. Equation 3.1 can thus be written:

$$\pm F.v_m = -I.\,(dv/dt) - F.v \qquad (3.2)$$

Now $\dfrac{dv}{dt} = \dfrac{dv}{d\theta}.\dfrac{d\theta}{dt} = v.\dfrac{dv}{d\theta}$ and equation 3.2 becomes:

$$-v.\,\frac{dv}{d\theta} = \frac{1}{T_d}\,(\pm v_m + v) \text{ or: } -T_d\,\frac{v.\,dv}{(\pm v_m + v)} = d\theta \qquad (3.3)$$

(the time constant T_d has been put in place of the ratio I/F).

When the motor is in action, equation 3.3 becomes, on integration:

$$\pm(-T_d)\,\{v_m \pm v - v_m.\log_e (v_m \pm v)\} = \theta + C \qquad (3.4)$$

where C is an integration constant. For the first part of the trajectory (using the $+$ signs) C is determined from the initial condition that $v=0$ when $\theta=h$ (the displacement given to the input element). The trajectory reaches the threshold line at the value of v given by putting $\theta = \theta_t$.

In the dead zone, when the motor is inactive, P and v_m are zero. Equation 3.3 thus becomes: $(dv/d\theta) = -1/T_d$. The trajectory is a straight line with slope $(-1/T_d)$. The value of v when $\theta = -\theta_t$ can thus be found: if it turns out to be zero or positive, then the trajectory ends at the value of θ when $v=0$. If v is negative when $\theta = -\theta_t$ a new value is found for the integration constant in equation 3.4, using the $-$signs, and a value found for $+v$ when $\theta = -\theta_t$ again: this defines the point where the reversed part of the trajectory re-enters the dead zone. The calculations are repeated until the trajectory crosses the axis of θ in the dead zone.

Ramp function input (constant velocity). When the input is given a velocity u, we have $v = u - v_o$, so that $v_o = u - v$. In deriving equation 3.2 from equation 3.1, v must be replaced by $(u-v)$.

Within the dead zone, $v_m = 0$. On integrating equation 3.3 with $(u-v)$ in place of v, we get:

$$T_d\,\{(u-v) - u.\log_e (u-v)\} = \theta + C \qquad (3.5)$$

Outside the dead zone the trajectory is described by equation 3.4 except that v_m is replaced by $(v_m - u)$ when P and v_m are positive (when the system is first released), and by $(v_m + u)$ when P and v_m are negative (after the dead zone has been traversed). The trajectory tends towards asymptotes which are asymmetric about the line of zero velocity, v tending towards $-(v_m - u)$ when P is positive, and towards $+(v_m + u)$ when the motor is reversed and P is negative: but its general shape is the same as when the input is given a displacement.

The integration constant C for the first part of the trajectory is found from the initial condition that $v = u$ when $\theta = \theta_t$. The value of $-v$ is found when θ again equals θ_t, and from this is found the value of C for the trajectory within the dead zone. If v becomes o when $\theta = -\theta_t$, the trajectory remains in the dead zone until $\theta = +\theta_t$: a new value of C is found from the value of $+v$ when $\theta = +\theta_t$. Otherwise, a value of C is found from the value of $-v$ when $\theta = -\theta_t$. The calculations are repeated until a limit cycle is reached.

Proportional control

The shape of the phase-plane trajectory may be deduced by starting with the characteristic equation of the system. Considering a second order system, this will be given by equation 1.29 (p. 159) which may be written as:

$$(D^2/\omega_n{}^2 + 2\zeta D/\omega_n + 1)\ \theta = 0$$

It is now convenient to use the natural period of the system as unit of time, and to write $d\theta/d(\omega_n t) = V = v/\omega_n$. (The relations between ω_n and ζ, and the stiffness (K), viscous frictional coefficient (F), inertia (I), and the time constants of the motor (T_m) and of the exponential delay (T_d) have been discussed on pp. 162 and 170). As before, we have: $D^2\theta/\omega_n{}^2\ (=dV/dt) = V.\ (dV/d\theta)$, so that equation 1.29 becomes:

$$V.\frac{dV}{d\theta} + 2\zeta V + \theta = 0 \tag{3.6}$$

The general solution of this equation, for any particular value of the damping coefficient, is complicated; but the phase-plane trajectory may be plotted with sufficient accuracy without finding the exact solution.

Suppose, first, that there is no damping, so that $\zeta=0$. The system will have a simple harmonic motion with constant amplitude and a frequency given by $\omega_n/2\pi$ c/sec. (compare equation 1.33, p. 161). Equation 3.6 becomes:

$V.(dV/d\theta)+\theta=0$; or, on integration: $\theta^2+V^2=h^2$ where h is the initial input displacement. This is the equation to a circle, and is the phase-plane trajectory of a simple harmonic motion of constant amplitude.

Secondly, when damping is present, the trajectory is most easily plotted by discovering its slope $(dV/d\theta)$, known as the *isocline*, at any number of convenient places. Equation 3.6 may be written in the form:

$$\frac{dV}{d\theta}=-\frac{2\zeta V+\theta}{V} \qquad (3.6a)$$

Along any straight line $V=m.\theta$ through the origin, we have:

$$\frac{dV}{d\theta}=-\frac{1+2\zeta m}{m} \qquad (3.7)$$

Thus, for any given value of ζ, we can find the isoclines where the trajectory crosses straight lines of various slopes, as defined by the constant m. These isoclines are the same whatever the initial conditions of misalignment, or rate of change of misalignment, at which the system is released, and are symmetrical on each side of the V axis.

The following particular conditions, also, are useful.

When $V=0$ (along the θ axis), $dV/d\theta=-\infty$ (except when θ also$=0$); the trajectories are vertical whatever the value of ζ.

When $\theta=0$ (along the V axis), $dV/d\theta=-2\zeta$.

When $2\zeta V=-\theta$ (along a straight line through the origin with a slope $-1/2\zeta$), $dV/d\theta=0$; the trajectories are horizontal.

If the damping is critical ($\zeta=1$):

When $V=-\theta$ (along a straight line inclined at 45° to the horizontal), $dV/d\theta=-1$; the trajectories are inclined at 45° to the horizontal and coincide with the line $V=-\theta$, which they reach, however, only after an infinite time. No trajectory ever crosses this line.

When the system is given an input displacement h, the trajectory starts from the point $V=0$, $\theta=h$, and V becomes negative as θ falls towards 0.

When the input is given a constant velocity u, equation 3.6 becomes:

$$V. \frac{dV}{d\theta_s} + 2\zeta V + (\theta - \theta_s) = 0 \qquad (3.8)$$

where θ_s is the steady state error. From equation 1.3 (p. 152) $\theta_s = (F/K)$. $u = 2\zeta U$, where $U = u/\omega_n$, as may be seen from p. 162. Immediately after the input is given the constant velocity, $\theta = 0$ and $V = U$, so that $dV/d\theta = 0$, as may be seen from equation 3.8: the trajectory will start off parallel to the axis of θ and the isocline is horizontal. In the steady state, when $V = 0$, $\theta = \theta_s$. If the damping is critical ($\zeta = 1$) the trajectory will be asymptotic to the line $V = -(\theta - \theta_s)$ as it approaches θ_s—i.e. as before, to a straight line inclined at $45°$ to the axes, but passing through θ_s instead of through the origin. (The misalignments are now all negative with respect to θ_s: V will be positive and the trajectories will lie above the axis of θ).

The effect of a threshold. The force exerted by the motor now becomes zero when $\theta = \pm\theta_t$ instead of when $\theta = 0$: when calculating the isoclines, $(\theta - \theta_t)$ is used in place of θ. If the system is critically damped, or over-damped, the phase-plane trajectory approaches the point $v = 0$, $\theta = \theta_t$. If the system is under-damped, the trajectory may enter the dead zone, where its shape is the same as in an on-off system. In order to plot this part of the trajectory the value of v ($= \omega_n V$) when $\theta = \theta_t$ must be known: this can be found by using equation 1.33 (p. 161). The values of the arbitrary constants are found from the initial conditions: for a step function input, $\theta = h$ and $D\theta = 0$ when $t = 0$; for a ramp function input, $(\theta - \theta_t) = 0$ and $D\theta = u$ when $t = 0$, and $(\theta - \theta_t) = \theta_s$ when $t = \infty$. If v fails to become zero within the dead zone, but crosses the $-\theta_t$ line, another portion of the proportional control trajectory must be drawn in the same way as before.

PROPORTIONAL CONTROL SYSTEM WITH FINITE DELAY, OUTPUT DAMPING AND A THRESHOLD

In a simple proportional control system with viscous friction but no inertia or delay, we have from equation 1.4^b:

$$T_m.v_o(t) = \theta(t)$$

where $v_o(t)$ and $\theta(t)$ are the output velocity and misalignment at time t. If we add a finite delay, the output velocity becomes proportional to the misalignment at some previous moment, the time interval being equal to the delay time, T_f. Thus:

$$T_m.v_o(t) = \theta(t - T_f)$$

where $\theta(t - T_f)$ is the misalignment at time $(t - T_f)$.

Two diagrams are plotted, as in *Figure 39*: (b) of position

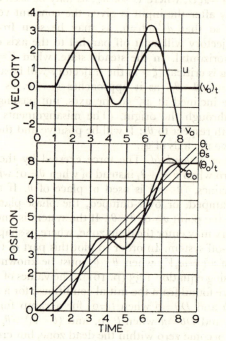

FIGURE 39 *Construction of the phase-plane trajectory of a simple system with a finite delay.*

(a) Input and output *velocities* plotted against time.
(b) Input and output *positions* plotted against time (in units of the delay time).
The output curves are built up progressively as described in the text. θ_o and v_o are the curves for the system without threshold: $(\theta_o)_t$ and $(v_o)_t$ are the corresponding curves with threshold. (See also *Figure 31*, p. 105).

against time, the input position θ_i being drawn as a straight line with slope equal to the input velocity u; and (a) of velocity against time, the input velocity being drawn as a horizontal straight line. The input position is taken to be zero when the misalignment has reached the threshold value; this is taken to occur at zero time. The dead zone is supposed to be so wide that the motor is not brought into action in reverse. It is convenient to use the finite delay time as the unit of time. In these units, from time 0 to time 1, the output position and velocity remain at zero, while the misalignment increases at a constant rate u. From time 1 to time 2, the output velocity increases at a constant rate, and at any moment is $1/T_m$ times the misalignment at the corresponding moment in the first time interval. (It is advisable to divide the unit time intervals into several parts—two have been used in *Figure 39*). The output position at time 1.5 is then given by the time integral of the velocity during the interval 1 to 1.5—i.e. by the area below the velocity—time line: the change in the output position between times 1.5 and 2, correspondingly, is given by the area beneath the velocity line between times 1.5 and 2. The output velocity at time 2.5 and 3 is then found from the misalignments at times 1.5 and 2—i.e. the differences between the input positions and the output positions as read from the plotted lines. The changes in output position are then deduced from the areas beneath the output velocity line from times 2 to 2.5, and 2.5 to 3, respectively. The process of gradually extending the output position line in successive small increments is repeated as often as may be desired. We thus have on one chart input and output positions, and on the other input and output velocities; from these we can read off the misalignment θ and misalignment velocity v at successive intervals of time and so plot the phase-plane trajectory which is shown in *Figure 31* (p. 105).

Non-linear proportional control systems

In order to illustrate the method by which the phase-plane trajectories are constructed, we will consider a simple servo system with proportional control, inertia and output velocity feedback. The equation of motion of such a system, after it has been given a sudden displacement, is:

$$I \frac{dv_o}{dt} = K.e = K (\theta - T_m v_o)$$

or $I \dfrac{dv}{dt} = -K(\theta + T_m v)$

v_i being zero after the system is released. (A similar equation would apply to a system with an exponential delay instead of inertia.) For plotting the phase-plane trajectory, we put:

$$v.\dfrac{dv}{d\theta} = \dfrac{dv}{dt}; \quad \dfrac{K}{I} = \omega^2{}_n; \quad \text{and} \quad T_m = 2\zeta/\omega_n \text{ (compare pp. 162, 170)}.$$

We thus get: $\qquad v.\dfrac{dv}{d\theta} = -\omega_n{}^2 \left(\theta + \dfrac{2\zeta}{\omega_n}. v\right)$

or, putting $V = v/\omega_n$: $\quad V \dfrac{dV}{d\theta} = -(\theta + 2\zeta V)$ \hfill (3.6a)

and we have derived equation 3.6a by a slightly different method. In the non-linear system, we have, similarly:

$$I\dfrac{dv_o}{dt} = K.f(e)$$

where $f(e)$ is used to represent e^n, or log e, or whatever function of e is appropriate. By analogy, therefore, in order to find the isoclines (slopes of the phase-plane trajectory) for the non-linear system, we must find:

$$\dfrac{dV}{d\theta} = -\dfrac{f(\theta + 2\zeta V)}{V}$$ \hfill (3.9)

If we can write $f(e)$ in the form of an algebraic expression, we may be able to evaluate $dV/d\theta$ directly. (In systems used by engineers, the non-linearity can often be expressed as $(e + \beta e^3)$). But if the algebraic expression is inconveniently complicated, or is not known, a graphical method may be used, the misalignment velocity, under open loop conditions, being plotted against the misalignment.

Suppose, for example, that the motor of the control system is a muscle. The relation between force exerted and speed of contraction is given by the curve drawn in *Figure 24* (p. 84): the inherent velocity feedback is not directly proportional to the output velocity. The isometric force set up by the muscle is, at least approximately, proportional to the integrated action potentials in the motor nerves: as a first approximation, also, we may suppose that this is directly proportional to the misalignment—i.e. the movement produced by the muscle and the deformation of some stretch receptors. The relation between misalignment and output velocity will then be of the same form as the force-velocity relation: after a step function input displacement, the curve relating misalignment to misalignment velocity will have the same shape. As a better approximation, this curve could be corrected for the non-linearity in the response of the stretch receptors, as given for example in *Figure 23*.

The procedure is illustrated in *Figure 40*, and is as follows. (*a*) Plot the relation between V and $-\theta$ ($V = -f(\theta)$) as line I. (*b*) Draw a straight line representing $\theta = -2\zeta V$ (line II). (*c*) Take any desired point P at $\theta = \theta_1$, and $V = V_1$. Draw a horizontal line PA cutting line II at A. The distance PA is then equal to $\theta_1 + 2\zeta V_1$. (*d*) Mark point B on the axis of θ such that $BO = PA$ ($= \theta_1 + 2\zeta V_1$). Draw line BC parallel to the axis of V cutting line I at C. Then $BC = f(\theta_1 + 2\zeta V_1)$. (*e*) From point D (at $\theta = \theta_1$) mark off towards the origin $DE = BC$. Join PE. Then the slope of PE ($= -PD/DE$) $= V_1/f(\theta_1 + 2\zeta V_1)$, and a line at right angles to PE defines the slope (isocline) of the trajectory at point P. The whole process is repeated, taking fresh points P as close together as patience permits, or as far apart as is thought adequate to define the trajectory.

The construction of the trajectory is somewhat simplified by the fact that $dV/d\theta = 0$ when $2\zeta V = -\theta$, whether the system is linear or not: all trajectories are horizontal when they cross this straight line. When θ and V are very small, also, the effect of the non-

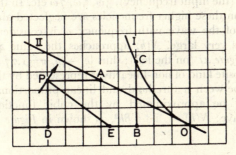

FIGURE 40   *Graphical method for constructing phase-plane trajectories of non-linear proportional control systems*

linearity becomes negligible: as the trajectory approaches the origin, it approximates to the corresponding trajectory of a linear system. If the system is critically damped, for example, all the trajectories approach the line $V = -\theta$; but in the non-linear system, the line which no trajectory ever crosses is not straight, but curves (towards the axis of V as θ becomes greater if the non-linearity is such that the gain increases as θ increases).

(4) NON-LINEAR SYSTEMS. FREQUENCY RESPONSE CURVES

The describing function

If $|h|$ is the amplitude of the simple harmonic input to the non-linear element, and $|n|$ is the amplitude of the output, we have:

$$|n| = \mathcal{N}(h) . |h|$$

$\mathcal{N}(h)$ being the Describing Function. If the non-linear element introduces a phase shift which varies with the size of the input to it, $\mathcal{N}(h)$ will be a "complex number", with a "real" part and an "imaginary" part which is multiplied by the operator j.

Suppose that a certain system saturates when a steady input reaches a critical value h_c. Then with an oscillating input, saturation occurs when: $|h|$. sin $\omega t = h_c$. When the input amplitude is very large compared with h_c (or if the system is "on-off" and saturates whatever the input), the output will have a rectangular wave-form, the instantaneous value at any moment being either $+h_c$ or $-h_c$. Such a waveform can be shown by Fourier analysis to consist of the sum of an infinite series of sine waves with frequencies ω (the input frequency), 3ω, 5ω, 7ω etc. In the Describing Function these higher frequencies are neglected and only the amplitude of the wave with frequency ω is considered. When $|h|$ becomes very large, $\mathcal{N}(h)$ approaches the value $4h_c/\pi|h|$, as shown in *Figure 41* (on the left); thus $|n| \to 4h_c/\pi = 1.27\ h_c$.

The opposite kind of non-linearity is represented by the gradual transition between a threshold and linear proportional control, which may be approximated by the cubic function $h + \beta h^3$. We then have: $\mathcal{N}(h) = 1 + \frac{3}{4}\beta h^2$, as shown in *Figure 41* (on the right).

Construction of frequency response curves

As explained in Chapter 6 (p. 111) the problem is: given an output motion (or signal) with known amplitude and phase, find the input motions (or signals) which give rise to misalignment signals with zero phase angle. With the system considered in Chapter 6

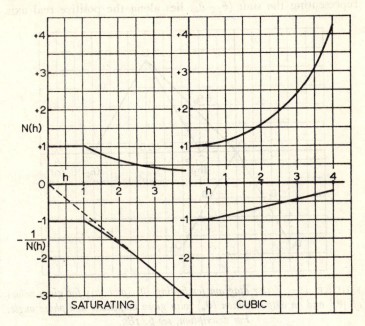

FIGURE 41 *The Describing Function, $N(h)$, and the Inverse Describing Function, $1/N(h)$, for two non-linear components, plotted against h, the input to the components.*

Left: component saturating at $h = 1$.
Right: component with "cubic characteristic" $(1 + 0 \cdot 2h^2)$.

it is not difficult to derive, mathematically, the required input amplitudes and phase angles. But it may also be done graphically, and if the system were more complicated, it would have to be done graphically.

On a vector diagram (*Figure 42*) the vector $\overline{OA}$, representing n, is drawn along the positive real (horizontal) axis, as reference vector. Some desired value of the frequency ω, say, to begin with, the natural frequency ω_n, is selected, and the corresponding vector for θ_o is found. (For the particular system considered, it may

be read from *Figure 14 (c)*.) This vector is rotated through 180°
giving the vector $\overline{OB}$, representing $-\theta_o$. A vector of length $|\theta_i|$
(chosen arbitrarily) is to be added to $\overline{OB}$ such that the vector
representing the sum $(\theta_i - \theta_o)$ lies along the positive real axis.

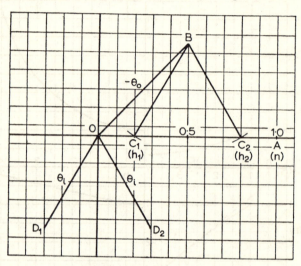

FIGURE 42　*Vector diagram for finding $|\theta|$ (and $|h|$) for given values
of $|\theta_i|$ and an output motion (θ_o) with given amplitude and phase angle.
For description, see p. 183.*

From the point B a circle of radius $|\theta_i|$ is drawn: where it cuts the
axis is the termination of the vector $\overline{OC}$, representing θ, of length
$|\theta|$. The radius of this circle must, of course, be large enough for it
to touch the axis, otherwise the assumed conditions are impossible:
if it is large enough to cut the axis in two places, there are two
possible inputs BC_1 and BC_2, with different phase angles and two
possible values of $|\theta|$. By drawing a number of circles, with
different radii, we can derive a number of different values of
$|h|/|\theta_i|(=|\theta|/|\theta_i|)$, and their corresponding values of $|n|/|\theta_i|$ for
the selected value of the frequency. The whole process is repeated
for other values of the frequency.

INDEX

Numbers in **bold** type refer to illustrations